Science Pathways

NI Key Stage 3

▶ Caroline Greer
▶ Iona Hamilton
▶ Jacquie Milligan
▶ Phyllis Vandevyver
Series editor: Martin Brown

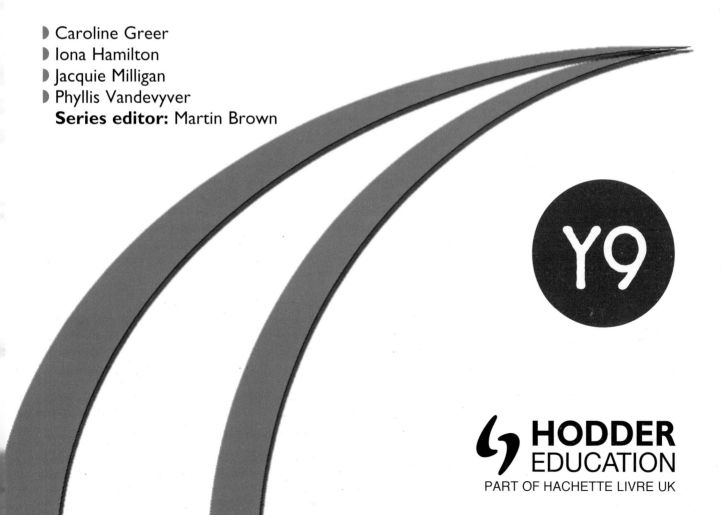

Y9

HODDER
EDUCATION
PART OF HACHETTE LIVRE UK

Although every effort has been made to ensure that website addresses are correct at time of going to press, Hodder Education cannot be held responsible for the content of any website mentioned in this book. It is sometimes possible to find a relocated web page by typing in the address of the home page for a website in the URL window of your browser.

Hachette's policy is to use papers that are natural, renewable and recyclable products and made from wood grown in sustainable forests. The logging and manufacturing processes are expected to conform to the environmental regulations of the country of origin.

Orders: please contact Bookpoint Ltd, 130 Milton Park, Abingdon, Oxon OX14 4SB. Telephone: (44) 01235 827720. Fax: (44) 01235 400454. Lines are open 9.00 - 5.00, Monday to Saturday, with a 24-hour message answering service. Visit our website at www.hoddereducation.co.uk

First published in 2008 by
Hodder Education
a member of the Hachette Livre UK Group
338 Euston Road
London NW1 3BH

Impression number   5 4 3 2 1
Year   2012 2011 2010 2009 2008

Cover photo: Alzheimer's disease, © Alfred Pasieka/Science Photo Library
Illustrations by Peters and Zabransky Ltd and cartoons by Stephen May.
Typeset in 12/14pt Geometric Slabserif 703 by Starfish Design Editorial
and Project Management Ltd
Printed and bound in Italy

A catalogue record for this title is available from the British Library

ISBN: 978 0 340 88883 4

Contents

Biology   Chemistry   Physics   Environment

Key Elements

The Northern Ireland Curriculum Key Stage 3 framework defines the following Key Elements and ways of attaining them in Science. Opportunities to cover these elements are indicated in **red** in the learning aims at the beginning of each unit of this book.

Objective 1 – Developing pupils as individuals

Personal understanding	Explore emotional development
	Investigate ways of improving own learning by finding out how the brain functions
Mutual understanding	Respect and cooperate with others in the process of scientific enquiry
Personal health	Explore physical, chemical and biological effects on personal health
Moral character	Recognise and challenge over-simplistic or distorted generalisations about science with informed and balanced responses, and take responsibility for choices and actions
Spiritual awareness	Develop a sense of wonder about the Universe

Objective 2 – Developing pupils as contributors to society

Citizenship	Consider factors that need to be taken into account when assessing statements that claim to be based on scientific research into issues affecting society
Cultural understanding	Consider how the development of scientific ideas or theories relates to the historical or cultural context
Media awareness	Investigate how the media help inform the public about science and science-related issues
	Explore some of the strengths and limitations of these sources of information
Ethical awareness	Explore some ethical dilemmas arising from scientific developments

Objective 3 – Developing pupils as contributors to the economy and environment

Employability	Identify how skills developed through science will be useful to a wide range of careers
Economic awareness	Investigate a product of economic importance to determine the science behind it
	Investigate a product to determine best value
Education for sustainable development	Investigate the effects of pollution and specific measures to improve and protect the environment
	Explore the importance of biodiversity, how it impacts on our lives, and how it is affected by human activity
	Investigate what can be done to conserve and promote biodiversity

Learning Outcomes

The Northern Ireland Curriculum Key Stage 3 framework for Science states the following Learning Outcomes, which require demonstration of skills and application of knowledge and understanding.

The symbols below are used in this book to highlight Learning Outcomes that are common across all subjects at Key Stage 3, and you may find these symbols in some of your other textbooks. There are three additional Learning Outcomes in Science that are equally important: practical skills, investigation and communication. You will have many opportunities to develop these throughout the *Science Pathways* course as you do the practical activities and investigations, and as you describe and explain your investigating and learning to other people by reporting, presenting or talking.

- Demonstrate a range of practical skills in undertaking experiments, including the safe use of scientific equipment and appropriate mathematical calculations.

- Use investigative skills to explore scientific issues, solve problems and make informed decisions.

- Research and manage information effectively, using mathematics and ICT where appropriate.

- Show deep scientific understanding by thinking critically and flexibly, solving problems and making informed decisions, using mathematics and ICT where appropriate.

- Demonstrate creativity and initiative when developing ideas and following them through.

- Work effectively with others.

- Demonstrate self-management by working systematically, persisting with tasks, evaluating and improving own performance.

- Communicate effectively in oral, visual, written, mathematical and ICT formats, showing clear awareness of audience and purpose.

Teacher guidance and activity sheets

A **Teacher's CD-ROM** (ISBN 978 0 340 94668 8) is available to accompany this Pupil's Book. It provides support for teachers on the new features of the Key Stage 3 curriculum, guidance on activities suggested in this Pupil's Book, answers to questions, printable activity sheets, and over 100 diagrams from this Pupil's Book for use with a classroom data projector.

In addition, the following activity sheets are available free from the website

www.hoddernorthernireland.co.uk

These will be helpful for pupils when doing a number of different activities, and their suggested use is indicated in the book by the symbol shown below:

X1   Famous scientist
X2   Investigating
X3   Media analysis
X4   Finding out
X5   Presentation
X6   Thinking skills: compare and contrast
X7   Debating
X8   Reviewing my learning
X9   Finding out about jobs and careers related to science
X10 Asking sensible questions
X11 Making a summary
X12 Finding the time
X13 Meeting the challenge
X14 Risk assessment
X15 Assessing reports
X16 Famous scientist or engineer
X17 Local scientist or engineer
X18 Using success criteria

Go to the website, click on **Science**, then on **Science Pathways**.

Atoms and elements

→ ## 1.1 What's the matter?

➡️ **In this unit we are learning:**

- that matter is anything that occupies space
- that matter is made up of building blocks called elements
- that elements are substances which are made up of just one kind of atom
- that an atom is the smallest particle of an element.

activity Look around you

Chemistry is the study of **matter**. Matter is anything that occupies space. Look around the laboratory and write down ten different types of matter that you can see. You can include things that you can see through the windows.

activity Classifying materials

1 Look at Figure 1 and study it for exactly one minute. Use a timer.
2 Cover the picture and try to write down as many of the objects as you can remember.
3 Compare your list with your partner.
4 Put the materials into groups. Decide what headings you could use, for example, natural materials and synthetic materials, or living and non-living materials.
5 Make a table to show the groups you have made.

Figure 1

Everything around us can be described as matter. You learned last year that matter can be solid, liquid, or gas. The air we breathe, the water we drink, and the ground we stand on are all different types of matter. It might surprise you to know that there are only about 100 different types of building blocks used to make up all the matter in the universe. These building blocks are called the chemical elements.

Figure 2

Don't tell me we're going to have to learn all that!

With just 26 letters we can make all the words in the English language. Words in all the languages of western Europe are made from these same 26 letters, and a few others. The number of substances which can be made from 100 different elements is so large that it is impossible to count them.

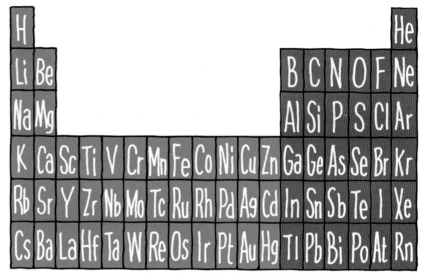

Figure 3 The Periodic Table.

What are these elements? Figure 3 shows a diagram of the Periodic Table, a classification of the elements devised by the Russian scientist Dmitri Ivanovich Mendeleev in the 1860s. You don't have to learn it, but you'll often come across this diagram in Chemistry. You'll find out what some of the letters mean in Unit 1.8.

activity · Looking at elements

Your teacher will show you examples of some of the elements shown in Figure 4a. Some of them are very dangerous so listen carefully and follow the safety precautions.

Be safe: Follow your teacher's safety rules

Figure 4 a Copper, mercury and magnesium.

b This bridge is made from iron.

You will already be familiar with many elements, for example, oxygen, gold, lead, iron, aluminium, copper, helium and silver. What does the word element mean?

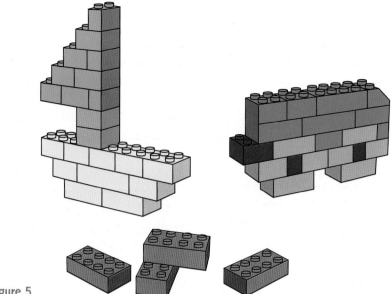

Figure 5

Look at the Lego® bricks in Figure 5. The red ones are all the same. If you were able to pull all the particles in a piece of copper apart, you would end up with them all looking the same. Scientists call these single particles atoms.

An **element** is a single substance made up of just one kind of atom. When different elements are joined together, compounds are formed. You will learn more about this later in this chapter.

Use a search engine to find out more about atoms and elements, to help you answer these questions.
1 **What does the word 'chemistry' mean?**
2 **What are the three states of matter?**
3 **How many different chemical elements are there?**
4 **Write down the names of ten elements.**
5 **What does the word 'element' mean?**
6 **What name is given to the smallest particle of an element?**

→ 1.2 What's a carbon footprint?

→ In this unit we are learning:

- that carbon is one of the main elements in the human body
- that carbon dioxide given out or produced by humans contributes to global warming
- that carbon is a black, solid element which exists in several forms.

Figure 1 A carbon footprint?

It is a big black footprint because carbon is black.

It has something to do with flying to places like America.

It is about the amount of electricity you use.

Figure 2 What do you think a carbon footprint is?

Everyone has a carbon footprint! This is partly because we are all made of chemical elements joined together in many different ways in our bodies. One of these elements is carbon and another is oxygen. When we breathe out we give out carbon dioxide into the atmosphere.

Another reason is that we use energy to heat our homes, drive our cars, and use our computers and electronic gadgets. Many of these things need electricity to work. Making electricity usually uses fuel which produces carbon dioxide.

Cars and aircraft use large amounts of fuel and as a result produce large amounts of carbon dioxide. This is also a contributor to global warming.

Your carbon footprint is your personal measure of how much carbon dioxide you make, and how much you are adding to climate change by the way you live.

Have you ever wondered what human bodies are made of? Here is a person recipe.

A young person weighing about 50 kg (about 8 stones) would have these elements in their body:

5 kg of hydrogen	1 kg of calcium
32 kg of oxygen	500 g of phosphorus
1.5 kg of nitrogen	200 g of potassium
60 g of chlorine	150 g of sulphur
9 kg of carbon	75 g of sodium

There is also about 300 g in total of copper, zinc, selenium, molybdenum, fluorine, iodine, manganese, cobalt and iron.

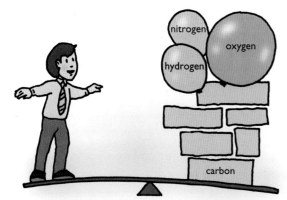

Figure 3 What are humans bodies made of?

Figure 4 There are various form of carbon.
a A diamond ring. **b** Graphite is used for pencil leads. **c** A chimney sweep sweeps soot from chimneys.

Let's find out more about carbon. As shown in Figure 4, it comes in several very different forms. Carbon is element number 6. It is represented by the chemical symbol C. It is present in all living organisms and is the main substance in coal and oil.

---

practical activity | **Burning bread to make carbon**

 *Be safe: You must wear eye protection*

You need: a Bunsen burner, a heatproof mat, tongs, a piece of white bread and eye protection.

1 Light the Bunsen burner and adjust to give a steady flame.
2 Use the tongs to hold a piece of bread in the flame.
3 Allow the bread to burn until it is coated in black soot.

Can you explain what has happened?

---

practical activity | **Getting the carbon out of sugar**

Be safe: This must be done by your teacher under strictly controlled conditions. You must wear eye protection

You need: a few grams of sugar, concentrated sulphuric acid, an evaporating dish, a heatproof mat, eye protection and gloves.

1 Put a few grams of sugar into an evaporating dish.
2 Set the dish on a heatproof mat.
3 Carefully add a few drops of concentrated acid.
4 Leave for about five minutes.

The concentrated sulphuric acid removes the hydrogen and oxygen from the sugar and leaves black carbon.

---

activity | **Your carbon footprint**

Use a search engine to find out how you can reduce your carbon footprint.

---

1 **What are the ten main elements in the human body?**
2 **Which solid element is present in the highest amount?**
3 **What is meant by the term 'carbon footprint'?**
4 **What are the three different forms of carbon mentioned in this unit?**

Extension activity | **More carbon**

There are other forms of carbon that are not covered in this unit. Use books or the internet to discover two more.

→ 1.3 How can we ask sensible questions?

→ **In this unit we are learning:**

- to ask appropriate questions to help us learn
- how to find answers to these questions.

Figure 1 Albert Einstein.

You'll notice that many of the units in this book start with a question. For example, Unit 1.2 that you've just completed asks 'What's a carbon footprint?' This is relevant because the idea of a carbon footprint is very much in the news at present.

Albert Einstein said that when he came home from school, his mother would ask 'What's the best question you asked today?'. You learn better if you learn actively rather than passively. Passively means you are simply listening or reading without participating. Actively means you are doing something – making notes, discussing ideas with others, thinking about questions you can ask.

activity ## Questions worth asking

Think back to some topics your teachers have explained to you. List two of these. Did you have a chance to discuss what was being said with other class members? Do you understand the topic better when you are able to ask questions about it?

For example, do you really understand what a carbon footprint is? If not, write down what questions you would still like answered about it.

The following passage relates to the effect on health of global warming, which is probably caused by the increasing amounts of carbon dioxide in the atmosphere. You will get some information from it, but there are probably more things you would like to know.

Climate change and human health

The climate we live in affects many areas of our lives. The quality of the food we eat, the water we drink and our homes are all dependent on our climate and weather. Some scientists have suggested that a warmer world will be a sicker world. While there is not complete agreement that this will be the case, the Department of Health has looked at the likely health consequences in the UK.

Climate researchers predict that the UK climate will become warmer, with hot summers becoming more frequent and very cold winters more rare. Winters will become wetter with heavier rain more common.

With winters becoming milder, there are likely to be up to

20 000 fewer cold-related deaths. However, there is a danger that bacteria will no longer die off during the prolonged cold spell, so that diseases may spread more widely.

More heatwaves will increase the number of hot-weather related deaths by up to 2800. Exposure to higher levels of UV light could cause an extra 5000 deaths a year from skin cancer and may cause an increase of up to 2000 cases of cataracts. Warmer summers may cause up to 10 000 extra cases of food poisoning each year.

Higher average global temperatures mean that diseases, or the animals that help to spread them, could possibly survive in areas that were previously too cold. It is possible that a mild strain of malaria will become established in localised parts of the UK for up to four months of the year.

Researchers have also identified other diseases, such as Lyme disease, cholera, dengue fever and yellow fever. These diseases could spread into areas where more humans live and therefore affect a wider population.

Globally, there are likely to be more floods, more droughts and more storms, which will be accompanied by damage to our homes, food and water supplies and will have an impact on our general health. An increase in flooding will promote the spread of water-borne diseases and the growth of fungi, while droughts will encourage white flies, locusts and rodents, all of which affect food and water supplies and health.

The World Health Organization and NASA scientists have been studying the relationship between outbreaks of Ebola in Africa and weather patterns. They believe that a rare climate pattern may precede outbreaks of the disease. However, the natural source of Ebola is still unknown – current thinking favours mice or shrews, although there are theories that favour certain plants. The time of year when these plants reproduce is directly linked to weather patterns.

Climate change is likely to have an unequal impact on the world population. Those living in poor and developing countries are going to be less able to adapt to changes. The effects on general UK health are likely to be less severe than in other parts of the world.

http://www.bbc.co.uk/climate/impact/human_health.shtml

activity Asking the right questions

On your own, read the passage, and then write down all you would like to know about the effect of climate change on human health. Select the three or four items you think most important. Make these into questions.

Now share your questions with the rest of your group. Write out questions for which your group would like answers. You can use activity sheet *X10 Asking sensible questions* to help you.

This unit concentrates only on asking sensible questions but, if you have a scientific mind, you will probably like to find answers as well. If you want to do this, you can use activity sheet *X11 Making a summary* to help you.

→ 1.4 Elements in the air around us

→ **In this unit we are learning:**

■ that the air contains chemical elements
■ that each element has its own characteristics or properties
■ how to make oxygen gas in the laboratory
■ some tests that can be used to identify gases.

Figure 1 The diver breathes underwater using oxygen from the cylinder, the balloons are filled with helium gas and the lights contain neon.

Figure 2 The gases in air.

Pie chart: 78% nitrogen, 21% oxygen, Other gases – helium, neon, argon, krypton, carbon dioxide, water vapour

Let's find out more about some of the elements in the air around us. The most abundant element in the air is nitrogen. It does not react easily with other elements. It is essential for life on Earth and is present in many important compounds. (You will learn more about what compounds are later in this chapter.)

The other main element in the air is oxygen, which we already know is essential for life on Earth. What does it look like? How can we tell the difference between oxygen and nitrogen when we can't see them?

Oxygen can be made in the laboratory by adding hydrogen peroxide to manganese dioxide, a black powder. The black powder is called a **catalyst**, which is a substance that speeds up chemical reactions without itself being used up. Hydrogen peroxide is a chemical which normally gives off oxygen gas very slowly. When it comes in contact with manganese dioxide it gives off the oxygen very quickly, and this is how we can collect some oxygen in the laboratory.

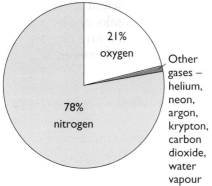

Labels: hydrogen peroxide solution, oxygen, boiling tube, water, beehive shelf, manganese dioxide

Figure 3 Hydrogen peroxide is added to manganese dioxide to produce oxygen.

practical activity   Making oxygen

You can use this method to collect several boiling tubes full of oxygen, which can be used in later experiments.

1 Put one spatula of manganese dioxide into a flask.
2 Set up the apparatus as shown in Figure 3 on page 11.
3 Fill several boiling tubes with water and place them upside down in the trough of water.
4 Half fill the tap funnel with hydrogen peroxide solution.
5 Open the tap and allow the liquid to fall onto the powder in the flask.
6 Let the first bubbles of gas escape, and then place a boiling tube over the beehive and collect the gas until the tube is full. Close it with a rubber bung.
7 Repeat this procedure until several boiling tubes of oxygen gas have been collected.

practical activity   Testing the oxygen gas

Oxygen is a very reactive element. It relights a glowing splint, and this is the test we use to prove that a gas is oxygen. None of the other gases in the air will do this.

1 Light a wooden splint using a Bunsen burner.
2 Blow out the splint so that it is just glowing.
3 Carefully remove the rubber bung from a tube of oxygen gas.
4 Put the glowing splint into the boiling tube and watch what happens.
5 Repeat the process.
6 Do this test again with a boiling tube of air, which is mainly nitrogen.
7 Compare the results.

Figure 4 Oxygen relights a glowing splint.

practical activity   Testing the pH of the oxygen

Last year you learned that the pH value was a measure of how acidic or alkaline a substance was. Acidic substances have a pH less than 7, alkaline substances more than 7. Substances with a pH value of 7 are neutral.

1 Take a piece of pH paper and wet it.
2 Put the pH paper in a tube of oxygen gas.
3 Watch for any change in colour.
4 Record your results.
5 Compare this with your results for air.

practical activity   Spot the oxygen?

⚠️ *Be safe:* You must wear eye protection

Use the knowledge you have learnt from the previous activities to find out what is in the mystery tubes provided by your teacher.

Another element present in the air is helium, the gas we use to fill party balloons that float in air. There is only a very small amount of helium gas in the air. It is one of the lightest elements, which is why it is used for filling balloons. Sometimes people inhale the helium from their party balloon and it gives them a squeaky voice. This is because your vocal cords normally vibrate in air which is much denser, and they can vibrate at a much higher frequency in helium.

Figure 5 These balloons are filled with helium.

activity   Comparing oxygen and helium

COLOURLESS GAS   NO SMELL

NEUTRAL: NO CHEMICAL REACTION WITH pH PAPER   RELIGHTS A GLOWING SPLINT

DOES NOT BURN OR SUPPORT BURNING   SIMILAR DENSITY TO AIR   MUCH LIGHTER THAN AIR

Use the descriptions given in Figure 6 to compare oxygen and helium. Copy each phrase and write O (for oxygen) or He (for helium) against each phrase. You might have to write both symbols against some phrases.

Figure 6

How do we separate the gases in air when they all look alike?

The elements in the air are gases. To separate them, first they have to be changed into liquids. The air is cooled until it condenses and is then heated up to the specific boiling point of each element. Each liquid boils at its own boiling point.

Remember the process of **distillation** from last year (*Science Pathways Y8*, Chapter 4). Air is separated into the different elements by using **fractional distillation**. The gases are then compressed into special strong cylinders. These are then transported to places where they are needed.

1 **What are the names of the elements which are gases in the air?**
2 **Which gas is present in the largest amounts?**
3 **Draw a diagram of the apparatus used to make oxygen in the laboratory.**
4 **Explain how you could show that a sample of a mystery gas was oxygen.**
5 **Why is helium good for filling balloons?**
6 **What is a 'catalyst'?**

→ 1.5 What makes elements different from each other?

→ **In this unit we are learning:**
- that each element has its own atomic structure
- that atoms are made up of three subatomic particles
- that the number of protons is called the atomic number, and tells us the name of the element.

Figure 1 These people are all very different from each other.

Look at the boys and girls in Figure 1. They are all 12 years old. They are also very different from each other, and from you. Each of us has our own **DNA** (**d**eoxyribo**n**ucleic **a**cid) which is a very complicated chemical made up of many atoms of different elements. It contains our genetic information, the information that makes us unique. You will learn more about DNA, and its role in making you the person you are, next year. However, if you want to know more now, key 'DNA' into a search engine.

In a shop each bar code (see Figure 2) is unique, and is different for each product. In the same way, each **atom** in an element has its own unique structure. Atoms are so small that we cannot see them, even with the most advanced microscopes. There have been many different theories about the structure of atoms dating back over 2000 years. Figure 3 shows pictures of some of the famous scientists who worked out the structure of atoms.

0 40821 19858 6

Figure 2 A bar code.

Figure 3 John Dalton, J J Thomson, Ernest Rutherford, Niels Bohr.

activity   Famous Scientists

You should work in small groups. Each group can use a search engine to find out what the four scientists in Figure 3 discovered about the structure of the atom and why this was important, and report back to the rest of the class. You may find activity sheet *X1 Famous scientist* useful here.

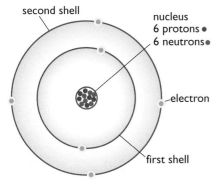

Figure 4 A carbon atom.

We now know that each atom has a centre called a **nucleus**. In the nucleus there are two different kinds of subatomic particles called **protons** and **neutrons.** 'Subatomic' refers to smaller particles inside the atom. A third type of subatomic particle called an **electron** orbits around the nucleus like the planets orbit around the Sun. However, unlike planets, electrons orbit in defined shells.

Figure 4 shows that a carbon atom has 6 protons and 6 neutrons in the nucleus. It also has 6 electrons in two shells around the nucleus.

Figure 5 Some particles have a property called **charge**, which enables them to attract or repel other particles. Unlike charges attract, like charges repel.

practical activity   Electrostatic charges

You will need: a plastic ruler or pen, a cloth for rubbing the plastic object, some small pieces of paper, some blown up balloons on strings.

1 Tear up a small piece of paper into tiny pieces.
2 Use the cloth to rub the pen or ruler hard for a few seconds.
3 Hold the pen just above the paper pieces.
4 Watch what happens.
5 Rub each of two balloons on the piece of cloth.
6 Holding the strings, try to bring them close together.
7 Watch what happens.

Rubbing plastic with cloth makes both the plastic and the cloth become charged. The paper pieces are attracted to the pen because the pieces nearest the pen become charged oppositely to the pen. The balloons move apart because they are both charged the same way.

Protons have a positive charge	+1
Electrons have a negative charge	−1
Neutrons have no charge	0

The number of electrons in an atom is always equal to the number of protons. This is because protons are positive and electrons are negative. Neutrons have no charge. When a proton with a positive charge is added to an electron with a negative charge the charge is cancelled out.

$$+ \text{ charge } + - \text{ charge } = 0 \text{ charge}$$

This means that atoms have no overall charge. They are said to be neutral.

Figure 6 The downstairs seats must be filled first.

1 **What are the names of the three subatomic particles?**
2 **Which particles are found in the nucleus of an atom?**
3 **Why do the electrons have to fill in the first shell first?**
4 **Draw an atom picture of oxygen, which has eight protons, eight neutrons and eight electrons. Look back at Figure 4 if you need help.**

The number of electrons which can fit into a shell follows a definite pattern. Can you think of a reason why the characters in Figure 6 must fill in the downstairs seats first? More energy is needed to climb the stairs. Electrons will always take the lowest energy level available. The first shell is at a lower energy level than the second shell. We now know that the first shell can only hold two electrons. The second shell can hold up to eight electrons.

What makes elements different from each other? The number of protons is different in each element. Carbon has six protons, nitrogen has seven protons and oxygen has eight protons. The number of protons is called the **atomic number**. This gives us very important information about the atoms and how they are likely to react with each other. We will learn more about this in the next unit.

→ 1.6 How do we sort the elements into groups?

→ **In this unit we are learning:**

- that elements can be sorted into metals and non-metals
- that elements were first arranged into groups of eight
- that the Periodic Table was first put together by Dimitri Mendeleev (cultural understanding)
- that the Periodic Table helps us to predict the properties of elements with which we are not familiar.

1 **How many of the elements in the Periodic Table are metals? Are all the metals grouped together?**

We are now going to look at how the elements are grouped together. On the wall of your laboratory you may have a large **Periodic Table** of the Chemical Elements. We looked at this briefly in Unit 1.1. Remember that there are about 100 different elements, and you will see most of these represented on the large wall chart.

---

activity What does a metal element look like?

Compare metal elements with non-metal elements. Head two lists 'metals' and 'non-metals'. Place each of the words and phrases in Figure 1 in its appropriate list.

(shiny)　(dull)　(hard)　(soft)　(heavy)　(dense)　(light/not dense)

(brittle)　(not brittle)　(feels cold)　(does not feel cold)　(makes a ringing noise when hit)　(makes a dull noise when hit)

(brittle)　(weak)　(conducts electricity)　(does not conduct electricity)

Figure 1 Words to describe metals and non-metals.

---

activity Identifying metals and non-metals

Look at Figure 2 and use the Periodic Table in Figure 4 to put the elements into two groups: metal elements and non-metal elements.

Figure 2 Which are metals and which are non-metals?

In 1866, John Newlands noticed that when elements were put in order of increasing mass, the ninth element in a sequence was often very like the first one. For example, starting from lithium and moving eight spaces forward, the element is sodium. Eight spaces further the element is potassium. He called this the Law of Octaves. These three elements lithium, sodium and potassium, are very alike and we could call them a family of elements. Let's find out how similar they really are.

Demonstration An element family

Be safe: Your teacher will demonstrate this experiment behind a safety screen

You need: lithium, sodium and potassium metal in their original bottles of oil, a trough of cold water, universal indicator liquid, a sharp knife or scalpel blade for cutting metal, tweezers for lifting metal, a white tile for showing the metal when cut, paper towels for drying the surface, a safety screen and eye protection.

1 Start with lithium. Using tweezers, remove a piece of lithium from the bottle of oil, and cut it in half to show the shiny surface inside.
2 Add a few drops of universal indicator to the water.
3 Use the tweezers to put a small piece of lithium into a trough of cold water.
4 Let the lithium disappear completely and discuss what happens.
5 Repeat this procedure with sodium and potassium, using fresh water samples each time.

Figure 3 a Potassium reacting with water.

b Alkali metals are stored under oil and have shiny surfaces when they are cut.

Lithium, sodium and potassium are all metals. They do not look shiny at first but when they are cut you can see the shiny metal inside. This is because they are very reactive and the outside is coated with a dull layer of oxide, formed when the metal comes into contact with oxygen in the air.

They all have to be stored under oil to protect them from the oxygen in the air. They are soft enough to be cut with a knife which is unusual for metals! They float on the surface of the water which is, again, unusual for metals.

They all react with water very quickly and turn indicator purple. This is because they all form alkalis with water. Did you notice that sodium was more reactive than lithium, and potassium was even more reactive than sodium? How would you expect the next one down, rubidium, to react?

This family of elements is now known as the **alkali metals**. The **halogens** and the **noble gases** are other families of elements. These families always appear in vertical columns which we call **groups**.

Dimitri Mendeleev discovered that sometimes Newland's pattern of eight elements didn't work. He thought that some elements might not have been discovered, and he left spaces for them. His Periodic Table was very similar to the one we use today.

Figure 4 The Periodic Table. The elements shaded blue are metals. The elements shaded red are non-metals.

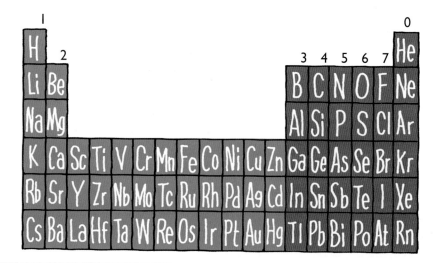

 ### activity Periodic Table

Your teacher will give you a copy of the Periodic Table.

1 Use colours to shade the alkali metals.
2 Use colours to shade the parts which show metals, and the parts which show non-metals. You will see that there are more metals than non-metals.

Figure 5 Dimitri Mendeleev.

The vertical columns in the Periodic Table are called groups. For example, the alkali metals are in group 1. The elements in group 0 are called the noble gases: remember helium, argon and neon are gases in the air. The elements in group 7 are called the halogens. The horizontal rows across the Table are called **periods**. The elements are represented by letter symbols which we will study in Unit 1.8.

extension activity Atomic pioneers

Use a search engine to find out more about:

■ John Newlands and Dimitri Mendeleev
■ the halogens and what they are used for
■ the noble gases and how they got their name.

---

2 **Write down the names of five metal elements and five non-metal elements.**
3 **Who wrote the Law of Octaves?**
4 **Describe what you would see when a piece of potassium metal is placed in a trough of water. What safety precautions must your teacher take?**
5 **Why are the elements in group 1 called the alkali metals?**
6 **What name is given to the horizontal rows across the Periodic Table?**
7 **What happens to the reactivity of the metals in group 1 as you move down the group?**

→ 1.7 Explosive reactions

→ In this unit we are learning:

- that compounds are formed when two or more elements are joined together
- that large amounts of energy may be released during compound formation
- that the smallest particle of a compound is called a molecule
- that compounds formed are very different from the elements from which they are made.

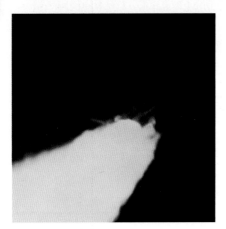

Figure 1 The *Challenger* disaster.

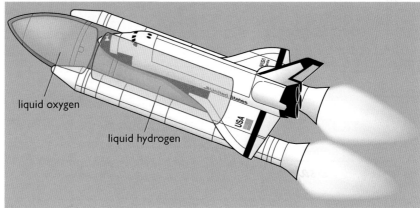
liquid oxygen
liquid hydrogen

Figure 2 The position of the hydrogen and oxygen fuel tanks on the space shuttle.

Many people all over the world watched with horror the explosion of space shuttle *Challenger* in January 1986. One of the seven astronauts on board was a science teacher called Christa McAuliffe. When interviewed before her flight she said: *One of the things I hope to bring back into the classroom is that connection with the students that they too are part of history, and the space programme belongs to them.*

Why did the space shuttle explode? Gas was leaking from the oxygen and hydrogen cylinders carrying the fuel needed for the flight. This ignited. The reaction between hydrogen and oxygen is explosive. The huge quantities of gas led to the terrible explosion, which took the lives of all the astronauts on board.

extension activity   The Challenger explosion

Use a search engine to find out more about this event.

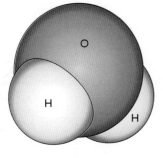

Isn't it amazing that when these two very reactive elements, hydrogen and oxygen, join together they form a **compound** called water, ice or steam? This new substance or compound can actually be used to put fires out!

The word compound means that two or more elements are chemically joined together in a **chemical reaction**. The new compound has completely different properties to the elements from which it is formed.

Figure 3 A water molecule. Note that there are many different ways to illustrate molecules. See for example Figure 5 in Unit 1.8.

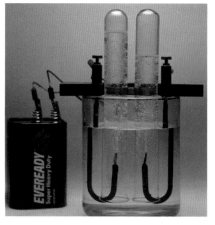

Figure 4 The electrolysis of water.

The reaction between hydrogen and oxygen can be represented by a **word equation:**

hydrogen + oxygen → water

Water is really hydrogen oxide. The smallest particle of water which can exist on its own is called a **molecule**. One molecule of water has three atoms in it: one atom of oxygen and two atoms of hydrogen.

Once a compound has been formed it is very difficult to separate the elements again.

Hydrogen and oxygen can be taken out of water in the laboratory by passing an electric current through the water, in a process called **electroysis**.

---

practical activity   Electrolysis of acidified water

⚠️ *Be safe: You must wear eye protection*

This activity shows how water can be separated into hydrogen and oxygen.

1   Set up the apparatus as shown in Figure 4. Pass an electric current through the liquid for about half an hour. Collect the gases in the two boiling tubes and seal with rubber bungs. Tube A, which was connected to the positive pole of the power supply, contains gas A. Tube B, which was connected to the negative pole of the power supply, contains gas B.
2   Test the gases produced. Do you remember the test for oxygen gas from Unit 1.3? It relights a glowing splint. The test for hydrogen is as follows. Hold a burning wooden splint at the mouth of a boiling tube of gas. If the gas is hydrogen you will hear a squeaky pop. This is a tiny explosion!

Figure 5 The reaction of sodium and chlorine.

When a glowing splint is put into the boiling tube containing gas A, it burns up brightly, showing that the gas is oxygen. When a burning wooden splint is held at the mouth of the boiling tube containing gas B, a loud squeaky pop or miniature explosion is clearly heard, indicating hydrogen. It can even make you jump! This shows that we can get the elements out of water, but it is not an easy process.

Here is an example of another explosive reaction. Sodium is the very reactive metal which you met in the previous unit. It has to be stored under oil to keep it away from the oxygen in the air. Chlorine is found on the opposite side of the Periodic Table in group 7. It is a very poisonous gas. You may be familiar with the smell of chlorine. It is used in small quantities to kill bacteria in water, and you often smell it when you go to a swimming pool.

When a piece of sodium is ignited and put into a gas jar of chlorine, a violent reaction occurs and a white solid called sodium chloride is formed (see Figure 5). The word equation for the reaction is:

sodium + chlorine → sodium chloride

Sodium chloride is better known as common salt, which some people sprinkle on their fish and chips. It is a white solid, which does not react with the air and it is not toxic. Once again the compound has completely different properties from the elements from which it is made.

practical activity — Making compounds

Be safe: You must wear eye protection. Do not handle hot chemicals with your bare hands. Do not stare at the magnesium reaction

You need the following chemicals: magnesium ribbon, granulated zinc, copper turnings, carbon (in charcoal form), gas jars of oxygen. You also need a Bunsen burner, heatproof mats, a combustion spoon and eye protection.

1 Heat the substance in a combustion spoon until it starts to burn or gets very hot.
2 Carefully lower the combustion spoon into a gas jar of oxygen gas.
3 Watch the reaction and record your results in a table.

All these elements react with oxygen to form compounds called **oxides.**

Figure 6 Discussing a reaction.

1 **What does the word 'compound' mean?**
2 **What is a 'molecule'?**
3 **Write a word equation for the reaction between magnesium and oxygen.**
4 **Draw a picture of a water molecule.**

→ 1.8 Can you crack the code?

→ **In this unit we are learning:**

- that each element has a unique chemical symbol
- that chemical symbols are recognised internationally
- that in compounds the elements are present in fixed proportions
- that each compound is represented by a chemical formula
- the importance of being accurate when recording chemical formulae.

Figure 1

---

activity Texting

**LOL RUOK
THX CU L8R EZ**

Figure 2 Texts.

Have you ever written a message to your friend in code? What about sending texts on your mobile phone? What do the texts in Figure 2 mean? Match them to the following meanings: **1** Are you OK? **2** Thanks **3** Easy **4** See you later **5** Laugh out loud.

There are so many different chemical substances, many of which have long complicated names, that it is necessary to have a shorthand way of writing down information. Chemists have their own code which is made up of **chemical symbols** and chemical formulae. Often they are written as chemical equations to show what happens during a chemical reaction.

For example, the basic unit of a substance called polytetrafluoroethene has the **chemical formula** C_2F_4. This substance is the non-stick material on the surface of frying pans! Polytetrafluoroethene is a **polymer**, which is made up of a long string of these basic units.

The symbols are identical in Periodic Tables from European countries. The spelling of the words is different because they are different languages. We are going to learn how to use these symbols which are like a chemical code.

Group number and Name	Group 1 The Alkali Metals	Group 2	Group 3	Group 4	Group 5	Group 6	Group 7 The Halogens	Group Noble Gases
Period 1	$_1$H hydrogen doesn't really fit in any group							$_2$He
Period 2	$_3$Li	$_4$Be	$_5$B	$_6$C	$_7$N	$_8$O	$_9$F	$_{10}$Ne
Period 3	$_{11}$Na	$_{12}$Mg	$_{13}$Al	$_{14}$Si	$_{15}$P	$_{16}$S	$_{17}$Cl	$_{18}$Ar
Period 4	$_{19}$K	$_{20}$Ca						

Figure 3 The first 20 elements of the Periodic Table.

Number	Element	Symbol
1	Hydrogen	H
2	Helium	He
3	Lithium	Li
4	Beryllium	Be
5	Boron	B
6	Carbon	C
7	Nitrogen	N
8	Oxygen	O
9	Fluorine	F
10	Neon	Ne
11	Sodium	Na
12	Magnesium	Mg
13	Aluminium	Al
14	Silicon	Si
15	Phosphorus	P
16	Sulphur	S
17	Chlorine	Cl
18	Argon	Ar
19	Potassium	K
20	Calcium	Ca

Table 1

We will look at the first 20 elements listed in Table 1, because these elements make up most of the matter in the universe. The elements have been put into a fun song, which you can listen to on the internet. Your teacher will give you the website.

What are the rules for writing chemical symbols?
- The first letter is always a capital letter.
- If the symbol has two letters the second letter is always a small letter.
- The first letter is often the same as the first letter of the name of the element.

Can you spot the elements which do not fit this pattern? Sodium was discovered by the Romans who spoke latin. The latin word for sodium is natrium. That is why sodium has the chemical symbol Na. Potassium was called katrium in latin, so its symbol is K.

Sometimes two or more atoms of the same element join together to form a **molecule**.

You have heard of the ozone layer which protects us from harmful radiation coming from the Sun. O_3 is the chemical formula for ozone. This means that three oxygen atoms are joined to form one molecule of ozone.

If there is more than one kind of atom joined together, then this is called a compound. For example, do you recognise this formula: H_2O? Water has a formula that is well known, and it appears as a logo on all kinds of items.

activity Finding out about elements

Working in small groups, use the internet to find out about some of the first 20 elements. Make a PowerPoint presentation with pictures to present to your class. Your teacher will suggest a website you could use.

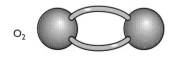

O_2

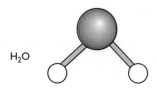

H_2O

Figure 4 O_2 and H_2O molecules. Two oxygen atoms join to make a molecule of oxygen.

The formula H_2O shows that there are two hydrogen atoms and one oxygen atom in one molecule of water. The ratio of hydrogen to oxygen is always 2:1. This means that the elements in water are in a fixed ratio to each other.

If there were two oxygens for every two hydrogens we would have H_2O_2. This is a completely different chemical called hydrogen peroxide, which we met in Unit 1.4 when making oxygen gas in the laboratory.

Here is another example of a compound. Carbon dioxide has the chemical formula: CO_2.

Can you work out how many atoms are in the molecule in Figure 5? It has one carbon and two oxygen atoms.

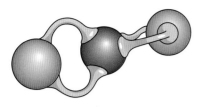

Figure 5 A model of a carbon dioxide molecule.

Rules for writing formulae for compounds

It is very important to write formulae correctly. It is just like entering a password. If you get even the case of the letters wrong in the password you may not be able to proceed further!

Look at these examples:

CO_2 CO   Co
carbon dioxide   carbon monoxide   cobalt

If you write a small 'o', carbon monoxide becomes cobalt.

Many compounds have a metal element in them. For example, table salt is sodium chloride. You have already learnt that sodium is a metal. The formula for sodium chloride is NaCl. The non-metal part will change to have '...ide' at the end. Chlorine has its name changed to chloride. Oxygen becomes oxide. Sulphur becomes sulphide.

If there is a metal in the name, always write the metal part first. Make sure you write the symbols properly with capital and small letters. Put the numbers as subscripts as you have seen in the examples.

---

activity   Chemical formulae

1 Try to write formulae for the following compounds:
   a magnesium oxide **b** sulphur dioxide **c** calcium sulphide.
2 Aluminium oxide has two aluminium atoms and three oxygen atoms in one molecule. Can you write its chemical formula?

---

1 **Decide which of the following statements are false and which are true.**
   – **All gases are elements.**
   – **Very few elements are liquids at room temperature.**
   – **Water is an element made of hydrogen and oxygen.**
   – **Helium has only got one sort of atom.**
   – **Sodium is an element with the symbol S.**
   – **Hydrogen is the lightest element.**
   – **There are more metals than non-metals.**
   – **Carbon dioxide is a compound.**
2 **How many atoms are there in each of these molecules?**
   CH_4 H_2SO_4 NH_3 H_2 $CuSO_4$
3 **Can you give names to these compounds?**
   Na_2O KCl   MgS   CaO   LiCl

2 Switch on to electricity

→ 2.1 Why is electricity so useful?

→ **In this unit, we are learning:**

- that electrical energy can be changed into other forms of energy
- the importance of the Law of Conservation of Energy
- to reflect on lifestyle choices with regard to electricity consumption (sustainable development).

In Unit 8.4 of *Science Pathways Y8* you learned about the Law of **Conservation of Energy**. This law is extremely important in science. It is always true. It says that energy is never used up. It changes from one form to another, and when it does so:

Figure 1 The Law of Conservation of Energy.

| total amount of energy at the start | = | total amount of energy at the end |

Figure 2 What energy conversions are taking place here?

Electricity is a very important form of energy. It can be changed into many other types of useful energy. A television set is an example of an electrical device, which changes electricity into other forms of energy. It changes electricity into light and sound energy.

However, to what other, less useful, forms of energy does it change electricity? What do you feel if you put your hand above a switched on television set?

activity Energy transformation

Look at the house in Figure 3, with many typical activities involving electrical equipment. Copy and complete Table 1 to show electrical devices and their energy transformations from electrical energy to both useful and unwanted forms of energy.

Figure 3 How many uses of electricity can you see?

Electrical device	Useful energy changes Electrical energy →	Unwanted energy changes Electrical energy →
hairdryer	heat + kinetic	sound

Table 1

You'll notice that, in many of these appliances, heat energy is an unwanted form of energy. Unfortunately this heat energy becomes spread out all over the house, and it is difficult to convert it back into other useful forms of energy. If you go on a journey by car or aeroplane, the unwanted heat energy from the engines is spread out all over the Earth's atmosphere, and cannot be recovered.

activity Have we put all our eggs in one basket?

We depend on electricity for most of our everyday activities at home, at school, at concerts, cinemas, indeed, everywhere. Sometimes the electricity supply can be cut, for example, in stormy weather.

Discuss with a partner how your daily activities would change if the area you lived in had no electricity supply for 24 hours.

activity Power cuts

Find out more about major power cuts, like those that hit New York and London in August 2003, and others which have occurred in countries around the world in the last ten years. Research one of these on the internet, and list its causes and the effects it had on people's lives.

Figure 4 In a power cut, candles may be used for light. Battery-powered devices are useful, too.

activity Reviewing your learning

Now look back at the learning aims at the top of the unit. Have you achieved all of these? If not, go through the unit again to make sure you understand all the ideas. Ask your teacher if you have problems with this.

→ 2.2 Where do we get electricity from?

→ **In this unit, we are learning:**

■ how our electricity is produced
■ to classify energy sources
■ to extract information from an internet report (media awareness).

Electrical devices need a flow of electricity to work. We call this flow an **electric current**.

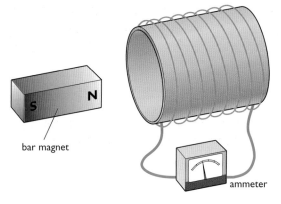

bar magnet

ammeter

Figure 1 Apparatus for making electric current in the laboratory.

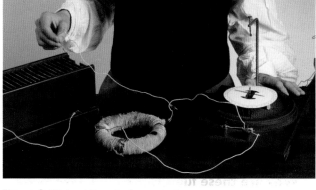

Figure 2 Michael Faraday's apparatus.

practical activity   Making electric current in the laboratory

Set up the apparatus shown in Figure 1. What happens when the magnet is moved into and out of the coil? What happens if the magnet is held still, either in or out of the coil? What is the difference? This activity gives you an idea about how the electricity we get at home is made.

activity   Bright Spark

Michael Faraday first carried out this experiment in 1831, using the apparatus shown in Figure 2. Find out about this famous scientist. Where did he work? What science experiments did he do? What is the impact of his work on us today? You can use activity sheet *X1 Famous scientist* to help you.

extension activity The Faraday inheritance

In a group, share the results of your research, and present a short drama production about Faraday's work.

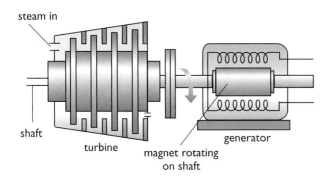

Figure 3 Steam rotates a turbine which rotates a magnet in a coil of wire to generate electricity.

Electricity is generated in power stations using very large magnets and coils of wire. All that is needed is motion between the **magnet** and the coil. The motion is produced by turbines. A **turbine** (see Figure 3) is designed so that when a fluid, like water or steam, flows through it, blades attached to a shaft rotate. This converts the straight line flow of the fluid to rotation, which can then be used to turn magnets. The turbine shaft provides movement in the generator, which makes electricity. It's that simple.

In general, if we have motion between a **magnetic field** and a piece of wire, we can make electricity. You'll learn about electricity generation in Key Stage 4. However, if you want to know more now, key 'Electromagnetic induction' into a search engine.

> Electric current is generated when a magnetic field changes near a wire, for example when a coil of wire moves in a magnetic field or a magnet moves within a coil of wire.

1 **Why are these fuels called fossil fuels?**
2 **Explain the difference between renewable and non-renewable energy.**
3 **List four sources of non-renewable energy.**
4 **List four sources of renewable energy.**

Fossil fuels

Most of the world's electricity is generated by burning **fossil fuels**. Coal, oil and gas are called fossil fuels. These are examples of **non-renewable energy** sources, because once they are used, they cannot be used again. Fossil fuels are burned to heat water to form steam, which expands and pushes the blades of the turbine around.

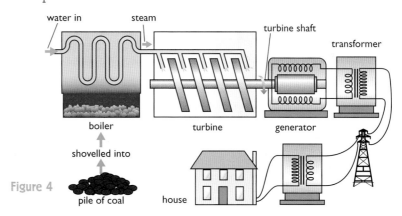

Figure 4

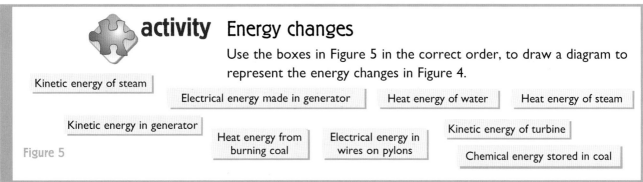

activity Energy changes

Use the boxes in Figure 5 in the correct order, to draw a diagram to represent the energy changes in Figure 4.

Kinetic energy of steam

Electrical energy made in generator   Heat energy of water   Heat energy of steam

Kinetic energy in generator   Heat energy from burning coal   Electrical energy in wires on pylons   Kinetic energy of turbine

Figure 5   Chemical energy stored in coal

activity   Energy changes

Figure 6 shows Ballylumford Power Station at Islandmagee in County Antrim. Fifty percent of Northern Ireland's electricity is generated here by burning natural gas. The gas is piped from the North Sea through an undersea pipeline from Scotland to Larne.

Work with a partner.

1 Discuss possible reasons why Northern Ireland's largest power station is located here.
2 If you could interview the manager of Ballylumford Power Station, what questions would you like to ask about the power station?

Figure 6 Ballylumford Power station.

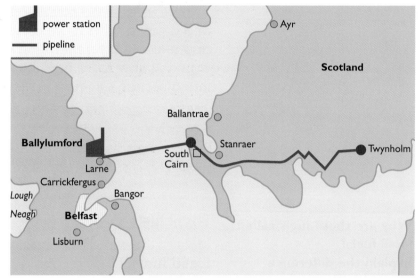

Figure 7 Location of Ballylumford Power station and pipeline from Scotland.

Coal not such an old fossil!

Using coal to generate electricity is back on the agenda in the twenty-first century as a serious player in meeting the world's energy demands. For decades fossil fuelled power stations have been widely criticised. Fossil fuels are non-renewable sources of energy, which means they are running out. If we use these fossil fuels at the present rate, oil is likely to run out in less than 40 years, gas in about 60 years and coal in less than 200 years. Also, fossil fuel release many polluting gases into the atmosphere when they are burned. Carbon dioxide is the most infamous. Scientists have designated this as a greenhouse gas which traps heat and so contributes to global warming. Sulphur dioxide and nitrogen oxide are also released, causing acid rain. Particles of soot are an additional pollutant.

Governments have therefore been encouraging the development of alternative sources of energy.

Coal contributes much more atmospheric pollution than its fellow fossil fuels. However, recently the debate has been based on how coal is cleaning up its act and can continue to meet the world's future energy demands. Its widespread availability and stable price compared with oil and gas have led politicians and industry experts to hope that the development of clean coal technology will make the fuel environmentally acceptable among climate conscious citizens. However, coal reserves are running out, and Western countries are finding that the remaining coal deposits are less accessible and proving more expensive and dangerous to mine. Unfortunately, alternative energy sources have not been developed quickly enough to meet demand, and coal is regarded as a very convenient resource, as it can be transported to inaccessible communities or areas with few natural energy resources.

China and India have large reserves of coal and are encouraging a shift in the debate from *should we* use coal to *how to* use coal.

activity   Problems with coal

1   Read the internet news report 'Coal not such an old fossil!' the whole way through to get a general idea of the information it contains.

2   Copy the incomplete spray diagram in Figure 8. Read the report a second time, stopping to record information on the diagram.

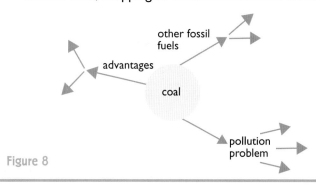

Figure 8

The Republic of Ireland produces about 15% of its electricity using peat, a plentiful natural resource. Unfortunately, it has all the disadvantages of a non-renewable fossil fuel and its extraction destroys many natural habitats.

activity   Energy from lignite

Northern Ireland has another natural resource: lignite. Research this resource and develop arguments both for and against its use in the Province. Make a PowerPoint presentation of six slides to record and communicate your research.

extension activity   The debate about lignite

Use Unit 9.3 of *Science Pathways Y8*, and the activity sheet *X7 Debating* to organise a debate on the issue: 'Northern Ireland should use its lignite deposits to produce electricity'.

→ 2.3 What's the problem with nuclear energy?

→ In this unit, we are learning:

- how nuclear energy is produced
- to consider different viewpoints relating to nuclear energy (citizenship)
- to develop informed opinions (moral character).

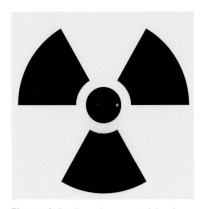

Figure 1 Radioactive materials give out dangerous radiation, which can kill or damage living cells. Our bodies cannot sense this radiation.

Figure 2 A nuclear explosion.

About 20% of Britain's electricity supply comes from a non-renewable source which is not a fossil fuel – **nuclear energy**. Nuclear power stations use the energy stored in uranium atoms. Atoms are the very small particles you learned about in Chapter 1. About ten million uranium atoms would fit across a pinhead. Nuclear energy is stored in the centre of the atom, the nucleus. A uranium atom gives out energy when its nucleus splits up. This is called **nuclear fission**.

This appears to conflict with the Law of Conservation of Energy that we emphasised in Unit 2.1. However Albert Einstein showed that mass is a form of energy, and can be converted to other forms of energy, just like kinetic or chemical energy. The mass of the bits of the uranium atom after it splits is less than the mass of the original atom, and the lost mass is converted to nuclear energy.

Nuclear energy is hard to control. If too many atoms split at once there is a nuclear explosion, like the atomic bombs that destroyed Hiroshima and Nagasaki in 1945. To control the fission process a special **reactor** is used. A lot of heat energy is produced, which is used to convert water into steam, which expands to drive the turbines in a power station.

The fuel is used up, but it still gives out dangerous radiation. The used fuel and old equipment must be stored for a very long time, possibly hundreds of years, until it is safe. This is called nuclear waste.

activity Nuclear argument

In 2006, councillors in Londonderry considered a local businessman's proposal to build a nuclear power plant in the city. As seen in Figure 3, the nuclear energy debate involves many different points of view. In a small group, discuss the following questions. There may be more than one possible answer to each.

1 Which of the characters has an economic argument?
2 Who has an environmental argument?
3 Who has an opinion based on hearsay?
4 Who is impartial and only states scientific facts?
5 Who has an ethical argument?

Businessman:

With soaring oil and gas prices, dwindling fossil fuel reserves and climate change, this is the best way to meet Northern Ireland's future energy needs. Without contributing to global warming, it will provide the same amount of power as 300 000 wind farms.

Government officer:

This facility could become a target for international terrorism and we would not wish to offend our neighbours in the Republic of Ireland who would be affected if a nuclear accident occurred.

Environmentalist:

Nuclear waste is difficult to dispose of and Ireland does not need a nuclear power plant, there are lots of other ways of creating electricity with renewable energy.

Scientist:

Living and working near nuclear reactors is completely safe unless there is an accident. Disposing of the nuclear waste could be achieved safely but it is very expensive. The best long term solution for the disposal of the UK's nuclear waste should be to bury it deep in the ground.

Local job market manager:

This will provide hundreds of jobs and provide a cheap reliable supply of electricity for small businesses in the area.

Local farmer:

Who will want to buy food produced on my land? Consumers will think it is contaminated and will give them cancers. I will be ruined.

Tourism Officer:

Nuclear energy is deeply unpopular with the public because of past disasters. People are frightened to be close to these sorts of facilities. It will destroy tourism in the area.

Citizen:

What do you think?

Figure 3 There are many different points of view in the nuclear debate.

Did you know?

In France 80% of the electricity is produced by nuclear power stations, and France sells 14% of the electricity it produces to other countries.

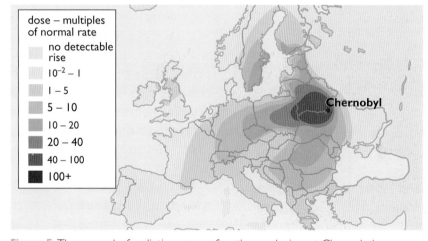

Figure 5 The spread of radiation soon after the explosion at Chernobyl.

dose – multiples of normal rate

	no detectable rise
	$10^{-2} - 1$
	$1 - 5$
	$5 - 10$
	$10 - 20$
	$20 - 40$
	$40 - 100$
	$100+$

Chernobyl

Figure 4 Chernobyl Power Station after the explosion.

 activity Chernobyl

Public opinion turned against nuclear power stations after the catastrophic disaster in Chernobyl in 1986. Find out what happened, and how radiation may have entered our food chain as a consequence.

  activity Why not nuclear?

There have been many more coal mining disasters, oil spillages, and gas pipeline leaks and explosions than nuclear power station accidents. So why is the public so afraid of nuclear energy? Discuss why people are afraid of nuclear power.

2.4 What's the alternative?

In this unit, we are learning:

- to classify energy sources
- the environmental importance of renewable energy (sustainable development)
- to compare renewable energy sources.

Solar energy
Solar cells convert sunlight directly into electricity. Solar panels heat water.

Wave energy
The rocking motion of large floats on the waves can be used to generate electricity.

Biomass
Chemical energy stored in fast growing plants is burned to release energy.

Wind energy
Air movement causes turbines to turn.

Tidal energy
Water is trapped at high tide by gates and released at low tide to turn turbines.

Hydroelectric energy
Water behind a dam is allowed to fall; the kinetic energy of the falling water can be used to turn turbines.

Geothermal
Water is heated by hot rocks deep under the Earth's surface.

Figure 1 Renewable resources.

Look back to Unit 1.2 to see how carbon dioxide emitted (given out) by cars, aeroplanes and fossil fuel burning power stations contributes to global warming.

Fossil fuels and nuclear fuel are non-renewable, and will run out one day. We need to develop other sources of energy which will not run out. These are called **renewable energy** sources, and include wind, tides, waves and hydroelectric generation (see Figure 1). Only 5% of our electricity is currently produced using renewable sources.

Gases like carbon dioxide and methane are called **greenhouse gases** because they trap heat energy, like the glass in a greenhouse. In December 1997, the UN Framework Convention on **Climate Change** was signed in Kyoto, Japan, by 171 countries including the UK. A series of targets for reductions in greenhouse emissions was agreed. Further progress was made in December 2007 with the adoption of the Bali Roadmap.

The British government has set a target of 20% of our electricity being produced from renewable sources of energy by 2020.

Renewable energy sources are generally thought to be less polluting than non-renewable energy sources, and they will not run out. So why are we not using many more renewable sources now? All energy sources have advantages and disadvantages.

activity Problems and advantages of renewable energy

Make a table and match the statements below to each of the renewable sources of energy shown in Figure 1. You may use some of the statements more than once.

Problems

- Land is flooded to make reservoirs.
- Tide must rise and fall quite a lot to be useful.
- There must be hot rocks near the surface.
- Natural habitats may be destroyed.
- Too many are needed to give sufficient electricity.
- Large structures will destroy the view.
- The wind supply is variable.
- Least energy produced in winter and none at night.
- Rough seas are difficult to work in.
- Sea water will corrode equipment.
- Must have plentiful supply of water.
- Solar cells are expensive.
- Drilling so far into Earth is expensive.
- Must be facing Sun.
- Unreliable supply.
- Considered noisy and ugly.
- Causes pollution when burned.

Advantages

- Free supply will not run out.
- No pollution
- Solar panels do not interfere with anything.
- Can quickly respond to changes in demand.
- The land can still be used for farming.
- Vast amounts of energy possible with rough seas.
- Low level technology needed.
- The plants used are cheap to grow.

activity Renewable energy for Northern Ireland

Discuss in a small group which of the renewable energy sources in Figure 1 could be used effectively in Northern Ireland.

1 How could each best be used?
2 Where could they be used?

activity Natural resources

Explain how natural resources have been used in the situations shown in Figure 2.

Figure 2 How are natural resources used here?

Figure 3 The world's first train powered by hydroelectric energy.

Did you know?

The world's first train powered by hydroelectric energy ran between Portrush and the Giant's Causeway from 1887 to 1949.

Figure 4 Water is stored behind the dam and then released to power turbines to generate electricity.

Figure 5 The Hubble Space Telescope is powered by solar cells.

Figure 6 Solar cells.

1 Can you think of some reasons why people might not want a hydroelectric power station near their homes (see Figure 4)?

2 As fossil fuels can be stored, they can cater for fluctuations in demand better than wind or solar energy. However, hydroelectric energy can respond more quickly to changes in demand. Can you explain why?

3 Why are solar arrays a good choice to power the Hubble Space Telescope (see Figure 5)?

4 Explain what is meant by the mismatch between summer supply and winter demand in solar cells (see Figure 6).

→ 2.5 What has all this got to do with me?

→ In this unit, we are learning:

- that individual actions can have global consequences (spiritual awareness/citizenship)
- that all industries have a range of jobs associated with them (employability)
- to reflect on learning (personal understanding).

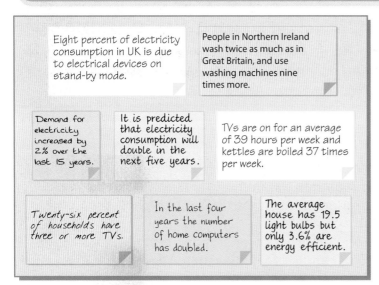

Eight percent of electricity consumption in UK is due to electrical devices on stand-by mode.

People in Northern Ireland wash twice as much as in Great Britain, and use washing machines nine times more.

Demand for electricity increased by 2% over the last 15 years.

It is predicted that electricity consumption will double in the next five years.

TVs are on for an average of 39 hours per week and kettles are boiled 37 times per week.

Twenty-six percent of households have three or more TVs.

In the last four years the number of home computers has doubled.

The average house has 19.5 light bulbs but only 3.6% are energy efficient.

There is a saying: 'If a butterfly flaps its wings in China, this can cause a hurricane in the Caribbean'. This refers to the idea that a small disturbance in the atmosphere anywhere in the world may multiply to cause major disturbances somewhere else. In a similar way, we all have some effect on the environment. By understanding the consequences of our lifestyle choices, we can act to protect the environment.

Figure 1 How do these statements relate to the environment?

activity Energy statements

Discuss the statements in Figure 1 in a small group. Choose one of these, and make a poster encouraging people to consider the consequences of their lifestyles.

activity Energy efficient

Research the term 'Energy efficient', and list ten ways in which your school could become more energy efficient.

activity Government priorities

The government has four priorities in its electricity policy:

- encouraging consumers to be energy efficient
- encouraging the use of a wide range of energy sources
- ensuring that there is sufficient electricity for everyone's needs
- reducing costs for electricity consumers.

Discuss these questions in a small group.

1 What do you think these statements mean?
2 Which would you see as the highest priority?

Nearly 100 000 people are employed in the electricity industry in the UK. There is a huge variety of jobs in a power station, from clerical, catering and cleaning staff to different types of specialist engineers – civil, mechanical or electrical. Physics and mathematics are particularly important subjects if you would like a technical job in the electricity industry.

extension activity Careers in electricity

The careers pages on the W5 website provide information on jobs and careers in electricity. Go to **www.w5online.co.uk** and click on 'education including careers'. Then click on 'careers' and then click on 'engineering and technology'. This takes you to a range of organisations that provide information on jobs and careers related to electricity.

One important job in a power station is to predict the likely electricity demand for each day, and for each hour of each day. The power station must be ready so that at all times the supply matches the demand. The demand can be affected by many things: weather, public holidays, popular television broadcasts.

People who control power stations can tell when a very popular programme is on television. When a break occurs millions of people make a cup of tea, and demand for electricity suddenly increases.

activity Energy demand

Discuss in a small group, explanations for the shapes of the graph in Figure 2.

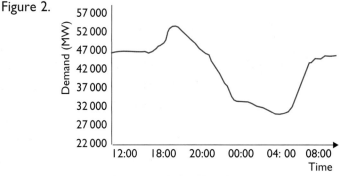

Figure 2 Typical daily electricity demand.

1 Choose what you think are the four most important words about electricity supply from this chapter. Write two sentences describing each of the words.

2 Describe how two renewable and two non-renewable energy sources depend on the Sun.

3 Why is wood both renewable and non-renewable?

4 Wind and the Sun are freely available so why is electricity from these sources so expensive?

5 What advantages are there in having power stations using several different energy sources?

6 a Are we being selfish in using up fossil fuels and not leaving them for future generations?

   b Are we being selfish in burning fossil fuels and changing the atmosphere?

→ 2.6 How can I find time to do my learning?

→ **In this unit we are learning:**

- to manage our learning time effectively
- to plan next week's learning
- to improve our learning skills by reviewing our learning (personal understanding).

Each unit in this book starts with the statement 'In this unit we are learning ...' followed by a list of aims, the things you should have learned by the time you have finished the unit. For example, in Unit 2.4 you were expected to learn how to compare renewable energy sources.

activity A typical week

1 Download a blank copy of activity sheet *X12 Finding the time*, or complete it on the screen.
2 Shade in on the grid: time at school, time for family and friends, games and social activities, sleeping and meals, that is, all the times when you're not free to study. What is left shows all the time during the week you can give to your school work.
3 If you have enough information to do this, allocate blocks of time in your grid to each subject. Leave some spaces blank for any unexpected work. This is now your general grid.

activity Next week

1 Print another copy of the grid and, referring back to your general grid, plan what you will do in each half hour block next week.
2 Organise a variety of activities in your study time: science and other subjects.
3 Stick to the plan as much as possible.
4 At the end of each week, look carefully at your grid and identify any areas with which you had problems.
5 Print a blank copy of the grid and prepare the following week's plan. It is useful to have a few blank copies available.
6 Try not to get behind, but if you do, don't panic: talk to your teacher.

You should set short term goals, like completing a unit in the textbook, or handing in a specific homework. Give yourself rewards (for achievement, not just putting in time): have a coffee break, go for a walk, listen to some music. Be flexible: review and change your programme if necessary. There may be some problems you have to deal with: you might talk to your subject or class teacher about these.

Use other 'bits' of time. Even five minutes with a book can be useful, but identify 'useful items' in advance. Keep a notebook with you. Note down things you may want to know about, or want to look up quickly on the internet when you have access to it. Also write down any questions to which you want answers.

---

activity   **Reviewing my learning**

Keep a learning diary to record what you have learned each day. Include reflection: if you have discovered a useful way to learn, note this down. You can use activity sheet *X8 Reviewing my learning* to help you with this. Build up a record of what you have achieved.

---

activity 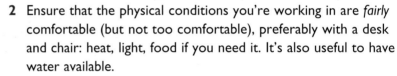 **Learning space**

Try to establish an effective learning space for yourself.

1 Decide where to study, and use this place consistently.
2 Ensure that the physical conditions you're working in are *fairly* comfortable (but not too comfortable), preferably with a desk and chair: heat, light, food if you need it. It's also useful to have water available.
3 Organise your space (desk/table, computer) effectively. Have study material and tools like books, paper, pens and drawing instruments conveniently available, so you don't have to go and look for them.
4 Keep other people out of your study time and space, but let them know that you're studying, and need peace and quiet.

Figure 1 Make sure you have suitable conditions to work in.

Figure 2 You can discuss work with your teacher.

Figure 3 You can work with other pupils.

You should help your learning by using <u>people</u> effectively:
– *teachers* in relation to course and subject material
– *other pupils* in self help groups, or by e-mail or telephone (remember, this should be two-way help: you can learn a lot by explaining a difficult idea to other people)
– *other adults* for support and information.

Always ensure that you take advantage of any school study support programmes.

You should also organise and use <u>resources</u> effectively.
– Your science book: *Science Pathways Y9*.
– Science equipment in school.
– Science information on the internet.
– Stationery and notebooks.
– Administration material, like school timetables.

Remember that there are different learning strengths and styles. Use your main style – aural, visual or kinaesthetic – as effectively as possible, but try to develop other styles.

There is no substitute for effective **time management**.

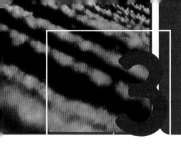

Ecological relationships

→ 3.1 We are what we eat

→ **In this unit we are learning:**

- that our bodies are built up from different substances
- that there is a healthy range of body masses (personal health)
- to reflect on what we already know about a topic before progressing to new information (personal understanding)
- to assess our knowledge and understanding by summarising what we know (personal understanding).

---

activity Remembering last year's work

This chapter begins with units on the elements and compounds that make up your body. You learned something about the elements in your body in Unit 1.2. Learning about this also depends on your understanding of some of last year's work. Check that you remember what is meant by: cells, photosynthesis and food chains before you start studying the chapter.

Figure 1 How do people grow from small children to adults?

What is my body made from?

In Year 8 you learned that water is a vital component of each of our body cells. About 50 to 75% of our body mass is water, depending on our body type. What else are we made from?

You have probably seen photographs of yourself as a baby or toddler. How did you get from that small person to the bigger person you are today? Where did all the extra 'stuff' that makes up your body come from? After water, the rest of our bodies are made up mostly from **protein** and **fat**, with some **carbohydrate** and a small amount of other substances such as calcium (see Figure 2).

All these different substances in our bodies come from the food we eat and the air we breathe. As we get older, our tissues and organs are built up from the food that we digest and absorb into our bodies. You will learn more about digestion and the different groups of food in Chapter 4.

water 42 kg

Mg Cl ⎤ other
Fe Zn ⎟
Cu ⎦
potassium
sodium
glycogen
phosphorous
calcium
protein 12 kg
fat 12 kg

Figure 2 Elements in the body of a typical 70 kg male.

activity

activity   Recalling cell structure

Recall information from Year 8, by drawing and labelling an **animal cell**. How much can you remember? Discuss with your partner what an animal cell looks like from what you learned last year.

Look again at the cell you have drawn. Did you remember to include a cell membrane? This part of the cell is made up from a special type of fat or **lipid**, with some protein molecules dotted through it. The nucleus has a membrane surrounding it and is made up from protein and a large molecule called **deoxyribonucleic acid**, or DNA, which contains our genetic information.

Each cell in our body needs carbohydrates to produce energy. Liver and muscle cells can store carbohydrates as a molecule called **glycogen**. We have already learned that the cytoplasm in our cells is made up mainly from water, with some other substances dissolved in it. All these different substances – lipids, proteins and carbohydrates – come from the food we eat.

Height	Mass			
1.75 m (5 ft 9 ins)	less than 56 kg (8 st 12 lbs)	56 kg to 76 kg (12 st)	76 to 91 kg (14 st 4 lb)	over 91 kg
	Underweight	Healthy weight	Overweight	Obese

Table 1

Some people convert too much of the food they eat to fat, and may be overweight or **obese**. An obese person might be 30 to 40% above the normal mass for his/her height and age. Table 1 gives information on a healthy mass for a 1.75 m person.

activity   Slugs and snails and puppy dogs' tails

There is a children's rhyme that describes what boys and girls are made from: boys are made from 'slugs and snails and puppy dogs' tails' and girls from 'sugar and spice and all things nice'.

1 Look again at Figure 2 on the previous page. The values given for water, fat and protein are for a 70 kg male. Work out the percentage values for each of these three substances in his body and record your results in a copy of Table 2. By adding these values together and subtracting the total from 100% you can also record the percentage for the 'other' substances.

2 Now add the following values for an obese man (100 kg) to your table.
   water: 47%, protein: 13%, fat: 35%, other: 5%.

Figure 3

3 Answer these questions.
 – How do your results for the lean man compare with the values for the obese man?
 – If you were the obese man's doctor, what changes might you recommend to his diet and lifestyle?

Substance	Lean man (70 kg)	Obese man (100 kg)
water		
protein		
fat		
other		

Table 2

Connecting with food chains

A **food chain** describes the flow of energy (and other substances) from plants to animals. All animals need to eat plants and/or other animals in order to obtain their food.

---

1 What name is given to these?

  a An animal that eats plants. Can you remember more than one term?
  b An animal that eats other animals.
  c An animal that eats both plants and animals.

If you and I grow because of the food we eat, how do other animals and plants grow? Plants are the only organisms that can make their own food, through the process of **photosynthesis**.

---

2 Can you write out the equation for photosynthesis you learned last year? What chemicals go into a photosynthesis reaction? What chemicals come out? Why is the photosynthesis reaction important to us? Note that this is a chemical reaction, since new products are made from the raw materials.

---

activity Reviewing my learning

Think about what you already know about food chains. Describe in about 30 words why green plants are important in the environment.

In any environment, all the animals are dependent on plants for their food. In a way, plants act as a 'food factory' to supply the needs of animals, by making many different substances from the **glucose** first produced in leaves by photosynthesis. We will look at some of the substances produced by plants in the next unit.

Plants and animals together make up the **community** in a particular place. All the different relationships between living things in an environment are known as **biotic** (or 'living') **factors**, for example predator/prey relationships, competition between organisms and disease. In Year 8 you learned how to estimate the numbers of a particular **population** in a **habitat** by using different sampling techniques.

The physical parts of the environment, for example the temperature, amount of oxygen, amount of light, rainfall, wind, pH and chemicals are known as **abiotic** (or 'non-living') **factors**. You will learn how to measure abiotic factors in Chapter 8. An **ecosystem** is made up from the community of different organisms and the environment they inhabit, that is, both the biotic and abiotic factors.

Figure 4 a A red fox feeds her cub in woodland.

b A fox scavenges in a dustbin.

3 **Write down the meanings of the following ecological terms:**
community, ecosystem, species, habitat(s), population, environment
Now use the glossary at the back of this book to check your answers and, if necessary, correct them.

4 **Practise your use of these terms by completing this paragraph.**
A woodland ……………... may contain many different …………… for example: shrubs, upper canopy, stream. A fox living in the woodland can have a ……………… of fleas on its coat. The fox provides a ………………… for the fleas. Together the plants and animals in the woodland make up the ……………... of living things. Sometimes foxes also live in towns and cities; they have adapted to an urban …………………

→ 3.2 A carbon-based life form

→ **In this unit we are learning:**

■ that many important substances in our bodies are made from the elements carbon, hydrogen, oxygen and nitrogen
■ that these elements are built into different molecules by plants
■ to investigate the effect of calcium on plant growth
■ to investigate an economically important plant product (economic awareness).

Substance	Elements
water	hydrogen, oxygen
protein	carbon, hydrogen, oxygen, nitrogen (plus small amounts of other elements including sulphur)
lipid	carbon, hydrogen, oxygen
carbohydrate	carbon, hydrogen, oxygen

Table 1 The elements that some important substances in our body are made from.

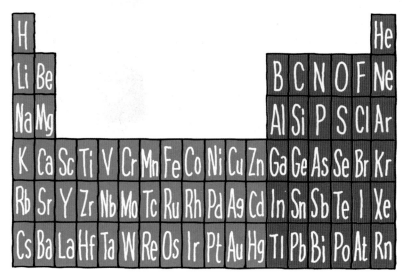

Figure 1 The Periodic Table.

Look back at Unit 1.6 for more information about the Periodic Table.

What elements make up the substances in our bodies? If we are made up mainly from water, protein, lipids (fats) and carbohydrates, what are these substances made from? Where do they come from? You learned in Unit 1.6 that all substances are formed from elements, which could be grouped into the Periodic Table. The elements in some of the important substances that our body is made from are shown in Table 1.

You can see that the elements carbon, hydrogen and oxygen are included in most of the important molecules that help to build our cells. Life on Earth is sometimes referred to as **carbon-based**. This is because the element carbon is one of the building blocks of **biochemical** substances. The term biochemical refers to a 'chemical' in a living thing.

activity Revising the Periodic Table

1 Find the elements mentioned in Table 1 in the Periodic Table in Figure 1.
2 What is the state of these elements at room temperature: are they solid, liquid or gas?
3 Which elements appear in all the substances mentioned (except water) in Table 1?
4 Are these elements metals or non-metals?

Figure 2 Ripe cotton bolls will be harvested to make cotton.

Like human cells, plant cells are also made up from water, proteins, lipids and carbohydrates. The main elements in these substances are carbon, hydrogen and oxygen. Nitrogen is also important for building protein molecules. Many carbon atoms can be joined together to make complex, long-chained molecules, called **polymers**. You'll learn more about some important polymers in Chapter 4.

You have learned already that plants are important in every environment. They are the organisms at the beginning of every **food chain**, and they produce oxygen that is released into the atmosphere, as well as making many types of substances that are useful for humans. Leaves are the sites of photosynthesis in the plant, but the roots are also important for the absorption of water and minerals.

I How does carbon dioxide get into the leaves of plants?
2 How does water get into the plant?

---

activity Specialised cells in plants

In Year 8 you learned about the structure of plant cells. Review your learning by drawing an annotated diagram of a plant cell. You should also recall that some structures present in a plant cell are also present in an animal cell, but some structures occur only in plant cells. Include these structures in your diagram.

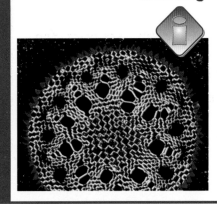

Figure 3 Light micrograph of a cross-section through the root of the plant *Smilax sp*. The purple cells at the centre are the pith surrounded by the pale yellow vessels of the xylem. The green area around the xylem are phloem cells. The internal cell barrier, the endodermis, is shown in white and red.

Plant root hair cells

Plants have cells in their roots that are specialised for absorbing water and minerals. Figure 4 shows these cells: they are called **root hair cells**.

The long, thin root hair extends out into the soil and provides a large area for the absorption of water and minerals. This is the special adaptation of this cell: the extra **surface area** allows the root to absorb much more water and minerals. If you germinate a broad bean and look carefully at the roots, you will see that the root looks 'furry'. This furry appearance is caused by hundreds of tiny root hairs extending out from the main root.

Figure 4 A germinating seed. Can you see the root hair cells?

Mineral requirements of plants

We know already that plants use carbon dioxide from the atmosphere, and water from the soil, to make sugars. Do all the substances manufactured by plants come from just carbon dioxide and water? In order to make proteins the plant needs some additional elements, the main one being nitrogen. Nitrogen enters the plant through root hair cells in the form of a **mineral** called nitrate. A mineral is a compound that occurs naturally.

Other minerals required by the plant include calcium (for building cell walls), phosphorus (for building DNA) and magnesium (for building chlorophyll). We obtain the protein we need for growth by eating plants, or by eating other animals that have eaten plants. So the nitrogen that was once in the soil becomes part of a protein molecule in the plant. Then when the plant is eaten, the same nitrogen atom can be built into a protein molecule in the animal or us.

Investigation — Investigating the importance of calcium for plant growth

Investigate the effect of adding calcium to growing cress seeds. You can germinate cress seeds on pieces of filter paper or cotton wool pads. Germinate the seeds until two leaves have developed.

Design an experiment to find out whether calcium affects the growth of seedlings.

Did the presence of calcium affect the growth of cress seedlings?

Figure 5 A 'physic' garden.

Herbal remedies

As well as providing food and oxygen, plants can provide us with medicines. The term 'herbal' means that the remedy comes from a plant. Aspirin originated in the leaves and bark of willow. Digitalis, a drug used to help patients with heart disease, comes from the foxglove.

Figure 5 shows a 'physic' garden. This means that the plants grown there all have medicinal properties. There is a 'physic' garden in the Botanic Garden in Oxford. In the past, the garden was used for teaching medicine. Each year, guides in the garden find that some children recognise a small pink flower called 'rosy periwinkle', because they have been treated with vincristine, which comes from that plant, for childhood leukaemia. The World Health Organisation has estimated that up to 80% of the world's population relies mainly on herbal medicine.

activity   Herbal healing

Do you live near a herbal medicine shop? Either find out about some of the products sold there, or carry out your own research about a herbal remedy. Write a brief report (about one side of A4) on a plant with healing properties.

Did you know?

Jesuit priests first brought the anti-malarial drug quinine to Europe in the 17th century. It is reported that Oliver Cromwell died from malaria because he refused to be treated by 'Jesuit' medicine!

Think – Pair – Share – Review – Peer evaluation is a way of helping you learn. First you think about an answer to a question for yourself. Then you share your ideas with a partner, and agree on an answer. This should be better than either of your original answers. When you then share your ideas with the rest of the class, they should be even better!

Figure 6 a Salix alba (willow).   **b** Foxgloves.   **c** Madagascar rosy periwinkle.

activity   Economically important plants

Research and write a report on an economically important plant product. You will need to decide on success criteria for your report, beginning with an explanation of what 'economically important' means.

Success criteria are produced at the beginning of a piece of work. They are then used at the end of the piece of work to evaluate its success. The criteria should be specific, measurable, achievable, relevant to the piece of work and have a time frame in which they should be reached.

Think: What do you understand by the term 'economically important'?

Pair: In pairs, try to think of a number of plant products that are economically important in Northern Ireland.

Share: Bring your ideas to the rest of the class. Decide which plant products you will research for your report. As a class, decide on the success criteria for your reports. In other words, decide what a good report should include.

Review: Read a report written by another pupil in your class. Did that person meet all the success criteria?

Peer evaluation: Write two positive comments on the report that you have read and then try to identify something that could have been done to improve the report.

→ 3.3 How to build a cow

→ **In this unit we are learning:**

■ about the work of scientists in helping the farming community in Northern Ireland (employability)

■ to investigate farming practice in the laboratory (economic awareness).

Figure 1 The grass is cut, dried, baled and then wrapped for storage.

A simple plant like grass can help to build a cow!

Many farmers in Northern Ireland farm cattle for beef and milk, which is then sold locally or exported to other parts of the European Union. During the summer months the cows can graze in fields, but in winter they are sometimes confined to barns, and the cattle are then fed on **silage**.

Providing silage is a way that farmers can feed cattle when pasture is not so good. It is a type of 'preserved' pasture, which involves the **fermentation** of cut grass to conserve nutrients such as sugars (carbohydrates) and proteins. In fermentation, the action of bacteria reduces the pH value of the silage to a point where decomposition (rotting) ceases, and the grass is preserved.

In Northern Ireland, farmers produce about 8 million tonnes of silage each year. Scientists in the Agricultural Research Institute (ARINI) in Hillsborough, and the College of Agriculture, Food and Rural Enterprise (CAFRE) at Greenmount, near Antrim, have carried out research over the past few years into the best ways to make good silage. This is silage with about 25 to 30% **dry mass**, 70 to 75% moisture. Dry mass is the percentage mass of grass after some water has been extracted, and gives a value for the nutrients available in the grass.

Table 1 Percentages of dry mass in specified conditions.

Conditions when cut	Dull sunshine	Dull sunshine	Average sunshine	Average sunshine
Length of time left to wilt	8 hours	32 hours	8 hours	32 hours
Single row	16	19	19.4	27.3
Completely spread	18.6	25.3	26.1	44.7

activity   A recipe for success?

Table 1 shows the results of research by scientists at ARINI on the effect on dry mass of:

- leaving grass in rows or spreading it out after cutting
- cutting grass in dull sunshine or average sunshine
- leaving cut grass to 'wilt' for **8 hours** or **32 hours** before collecting it into bales.

1 Discuss with a partner how you can best illustrate these results to help explain what they mean. Check your method with your teacher before starting your plot.

2 What conditions seem to give the best quality silage?

practical activity Make your own silage

You can make your own silage in the laboratory using a plastic drainpipe as the packaging for your 'bale' of grass. Your teacher will tell you where to find the method. You can vary different factors to assess the effect they have on the quality of your silage. Perhaps your teacher could invite a local farmer into school to evaluate the different types of silage in your class!

Government and research organisations provide information to farmers so that they can tell when the water content of their silage is most effective.

Assessing dry matter

In order to meet the target of 25 to 30% dry matter it is essential to be able to assess the dry matter of the crop at various stages. Walking through the standing crop should enable you to assess initial dry matter. As a general rule, if your boots are wet the dry matter content of the crop is approximately 15%. If, however, your boots remain dry after walking the field, then the dry matter content is approximately 20%.

The Department of Agriculture and Rural Development (Northern Ireland)

The optimum water content for your fresh grass is 60 to 70%. You can test this by taking a clump of grass and tightly squeezing it into a small ball in your hand, then letting your hand open up. Ideally, no water will come out of the ball when you squeeze, and when you open your hand the ball will slowly fall apart. If water comes out when you are squeezing the grass then the grass is too wet and it must be allowed to dry a bit more. If the ball falls apart immediately when you open your hand, it is too dry and some water should be added.

The University of Waikato, New Zealand

→ 3.4 Building pyramids

> **→ In this unit we are learning:**
> - to make predictions about populations
> - to identify patterns in feeding relationships
> - about relationships between organisms in a pyramid of numbers.

activity Remembering last year's work

Some ideas in this unit depend on your understanding of some of last year's work. Check that you remember what is meant by 'primary', 'secondary' and 'tertiary' consumers before you start studying the unit.

Introducing trophic levels

The flow of energy from grass to humans through eating beef products can be shown as:

> grass → cow → human

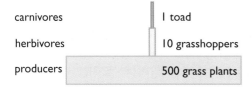

Figure 1 A pyramid for a food chain grass → grasshopper → toad.

Each organism in this simple food chain is at a different feeding level or **trophic level**, so the plant is at the first trophic level, the cow is at the second trophic level and the human is at the third trophic level. Of course many other organisms can also eat grass, not just cows. One species that the farmer may consider a 'pest' is the rabbit, as it is **competition** with cows for the grass in the farmer's field. Cows are called primary consumers as they eat plants. Humans who eat cows are secondary consumers.

Figure 2 A pyramid showing the relative number of organisms at each trophic level in a four-tier food chain.

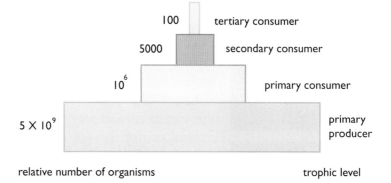

relative number of organisms   trophic level

1 **Can you predict what might happen to the size of a rabbit population over time if the cattle that normally grazed in the same area were moved to a different pasture?**

2 **Why might a farmer want to discourage rabbits from living on his grazing land?**

3 **How may grass and other plants benefit from having cows in their habitat?**

activity Identifying patterns

The following data were obtained for the numbers of organisms in two different areas of pasture in Northern Ireland.

In area 1, there were 10 200 grass plants, 65 rabbits and four foxes. In area 2, there were 15 600 grass plants, 114 mice and two owls.

What patterns do you see in the numbers of organisms? How might you plot these data? Ecologists plot data like this in a **pyramid of numbers** like those shown in Figures 1 and 2. A pyramid of numbers is a way of representing the organisms at each trophic level in a food chain. Note that the number of organisms normally decreases as you move up the pyramid.

In Year 8 you learned that food chains are short because a lot of energy is lost between each step in the food chain. We can now say that energy is lost between each trophic level. As well as explaining why food chains are short, the loss of energy between each level also explains why the numbers of organisms normally decreases as you move along the food chain or food web.

Unfortunately, pyramids of numbers for a particular food chain may not always be pyramid-shaped. Can you think of a link in a food chain where the numbers of primary consumers might be greater than the numbers of producers or where the number of secondary consumers is greater than the number of primary consumers?

---

4 How could ecologists have obtained the data for the pyramids shown in Figures 1 and 2? Describe how the population numbers for each level may have been determined.

Figure 3 Decomposition.

Now you see it, now you don't: the work of decomposers

Energy does not keep on flowing forever through a food web, eventually there is a final trophic level, usually a successful predator. What happens next? The animals at the top of a food web die, yet the process is not yet complete, for the substances and energy contained in a dead organism can be released by **decomposers**.

Dead organisms do not simply disappear, they are broken down by the action of small organisms, including bacteria and fungi. You will learn more about the work of these microbes in Chapter 10.

When decomposers break down dead plants and animals they release carbon dioxide through respiration. This means that minerals such as carbon and nitrogen are recycled back into the environment, for re-use by plants.

→ 3.5 Carbon forever

> **→ In this unit we are learning:**
>
> - that carbon is recycled in nature
> - to develop success criteria for a task
> - to evaluate and improve our performance by summarising and sharing knowledge (personal understanding)
> - to use our imagination in writing creatively about a scientific topic (personal understanding).

Recycling is not a new idea. Since the beginning of life on Earth, the elements that make up our planet have been recycled through different processes. Some of these processes involve living things. We know already that plants use carbon dioxide from the atmosphere to synthesise (make) sugars. Other animals can eat these sugars and use them for respiration, releasing carbon dioxide back into the atmosphere.

In a way, we can say that (for plants at least) carbon dioxide is 'the breath of life'. Using the simple substances carbon dioxide and water, with some minerals from the soil, plants can make many different substances as well as producing oxygen as a waste product.

activity What have plants ever done for me?

In this activity you are asked to review your learning of the different sections in this chapter, as well as recalling information from Year 8. Figure 1 shows a diagram of a tree. Draw your own copy on an A4 page. Around the diagram make as many notes as you can about the importance and role of plants in an **ecosystem**.

You can use activity sheet *X18 Using success criteria* here. What are the success criteria for this activity? Here are some points to consider:
- the role of plants as producers in food chains/webs
- plants as habitats
- requirements of plants for photosynthesis
- the role of the leaf
- the role of the root
- plants as resources for humans.

Think: Consider as many things as you can and include them as annotations around the image of the tree. Include any equations that may be appropriate.

Pair: Swap your page with a partner. Did your partner include the same information as you? Was there anything extra that you did not have in your notes?

Share: Swap pages back again and include any extra information. Discuss your ideas with the rest of the class. Did you meet all the success criteria for the activity?

Review: What new things have you learned so far in this chapter? Has anything surprised you? Is there anything you'd like to find out more about?

Figure 1 Why are plants important in an ecosystem?

Figure 2 The sugars in the strawberry are used for respiration, which releases carbon dioxide into the atmosphere.

The carbon atom in a carbon dioxide molecule may be built into a different molecule in the plant, for example, into a sugar that may be dissolved in cell cytoplasm in a strawberry. When you eat and digest the strawberry, you take that carbon atom into your own body, perhaps as part of a sugar molecule that you will eventually use for respiration inside your own cells.

Carbon dioxide is a waste product of respiration. It diffuses out from our cells and is carried, dissolved in plasma in our blood, to our lungs, where we breathe it out. In this way carbon travels from the atmosphere into the strawberry plant, then into our bodies, then back into the atmosphere again. Carbon has been recycled!

1 **The word equation for photosynthesis is:**
   carbon dioxide + water (with energy supplied from the Sun)
   → glucose + oxygen
   Write a similar equation for respiration.

activity   Sequencing

Make a series of cards showing the journey of a carbon atom from the atmosphere into a plant and then eventually back into the atmosphere again, using drawings or simple sentences. Include as many steps as you can, but not more than eight. Challenge your partner to put the cards together in the correct sequence.

Carbon has been recycling on Earth since the beginning of life on our planet. Perhaps a carbon atom that is in your body now was once in the body of a dinosaur! It's also quite possible that some of your carbon atoms once belonged to Moses or Julius Caesar, or any other historical figure.

activity   Creative writing

Write a 100-word story about the journey of a carbon atom through time. After learning about digestion in Chapter 4 you might return to this story to include even more detail!

→ 3.6 Space invaders

→ **In this unit we are learning:**

- to make inferences from scientific data
- to develop questions that may be investigated by a scientist
- about the work of some Northern Ireland scientists.

Figure 1 a Leonid meteor (shooting star) shower.

b A bright fireball.

c Comet Hale-Bopp.

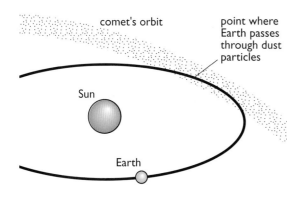

Figure 2 The Earth can sometimes pass through the orbit of a comet on its own orbit around the Sun.

Has Earth been invaded already?

Elements such as carbon are recycled in nature on Earth. However, Earth is not a totally sealed system, and objects *can* enter the Earth's atmosphere from space! There are different types of **extraterrestrial** invader that can enter our atmosphere, and even land on the Earth.

One of the photographs in Figure 1 is an odd-one-out: can you spot which one? The 'shooting stars' are actually small extraterrestrial particles that are burnt up as they streak through our atmosphere. According to the British Astronomical Association (BAA), a fireball is technically 'any meteor brighter than the planet Venus'. The **comet** is the odd-one-out, as it is not actually in the Earth's atmosphere, but can be so bright that we can observe it as it sweeps through space and orbits the Sun.

Comets, sometimes described as 'dirty snowballs', are thought to fall in towards the Sun from far out in the Solar System, beyond even the orbit of Pluto. You learned a little about comets in Year 8. A disturbance of some sort sends the comet plunging in towards the Sun and, as it gets nearer to our star, the comet begins to evaporate. Parts of the comet stream out behind it as it hurtles nearer and nearer to the heat of the Sun.

The comet can leave this 'dust trail' behind it in space. Figure 2 shows that the Earth can sometimes pass through the dusty path of a comet on its own orbit around the Sun. When this happens the bits of dust and debris get captured by the gravity of Earth, and burn up due to friction with the atmosphere, resulting in 'shooting stars'.

The Earth passes through several cometary dust trails every year. Astronomers can even predict when we are more likely to see shooting stars, or **meteors**, as we pass through the known path of a comet, for example in August you can look out for the Perseids, or in November, the Leonid meteors (see Figure 1). Dr David Asher, an astronomer at Armagh Observatory, is famous for his accurate predictions about the timing of the Leonid meteors.

---

activity What's in a name?

A meteor that lands on the Earth is known as a **meteorite.** Only a small number of meteorites come from comets: most originate from pieces of **asteroids**. Thus, meteors are important for scientists because their chemical analysis can tell us about the ancient objects that may be similar to the material from which our Solar System was formed.

1 You will come across different terms when you read about 'shooting stars'. Using a dictionary, astronomy book or search engine, find out what the difference is between a meteoroid, a meteor and a meteorite. Write the definitions of each into your notes.
2 Learn about the classification of meteors. Your teacher will give you some useful websites.

You can also use a search engine, or books from the school library to find out more. Using the information that you gather, make a set of cards that will allow identification of different types of meteor.

Figure 3 Trees damaged in the Tunguska event.

Making inferences

Scientists know that some comets have not just passed by the Earth on their journey around the Sun, but have actually collided with Earth. In 1908 a meteor exploded in the air above Tunguska, a wooded area in Siberia, blasting trees throughout an area of 2000 km^2 in an explosion that was the equivalent of one thousand atomic bombs (see Figure 3). Various chemicals were found in the atmosphere after this impact event. Scientists believe that some of these chemicals destroyed about one third of the ozone layer around the Earth.

Professor Mike Baillie from the Department of Archaeology and Palaeoecology at Queen's University Belfast, has asked questions about the effect of extraterrestrial impact events on human populations. He describes as 'educated speculation' his theories linking impact events with the huge death toll in the fourteenth century, when the 'Black Death' swept through Europe.

The key thing about Professor Baillie's theories, though, is that he bases them on 'a host of scientific evidence'. Some of the evidence is held as a 'history' in trees. The evidence also includes early writings about the Black Death.

- Tree rings show that there was a downturn in growth of trees in different places around the world, showing that this was a global event.
- Carbon dioxide levels in the atmosphere changed (evidence from ice-cores, which are taken from ice in the Arctic or Antarctic).
- Amounts of ammonia in the atmosphere increased (from ice-core data) in a similar way as they did after the Tunguska event.
- Early writers describe 'fire from heaven' and the occurrence of comets and earthquakes before the outbreak of the plague.
- Many writers describe a 'corrupted atmosphere', a 'pestiferous wind' and a 'poisonous odour'.
- The term *pestilència* can mean 'something coming on us from the stars'.

Professor Baillie links dated evidence from different sources to come up with a new idea, that is, he makes **inferences** from the evidence. You can find out more about this in *New light on the Black Death The Cosmic Connection*, Mike Baillie, ISBN 0 7524 3598 1.

---

activity Meteorite strike

A meteorite lands near a remote village. A few days later some of the children develop a severe cough and a high temperature. You are sent to the village as part of the 'Disease Analysis Research Team' (DART) to determine the cause of the children's symptoms.

Work in a group. Decide on the roles of each DART member.
1 What questions might you need to ask?
2 What preparations would you have to make?
3 What tests could you carry out?
4 What other experts might you need to consult?

Before you leave for the village, your team is required to give a press conference. Create a five-minute presentation to outline your plans and explain your decisions.

→ 3.7 Meeting the challenge

→ In this unit we are learning:

- to refine a general issue into a series of specific investigations
- to present a report on a science issue.

Figure 1 Cassiopeia constellation.

Figure 2 a A pupil works at a telescope.

b An astronomer in a telescope control room.

In school you often do investigations to help you find out about scientific themes. Sometimes these are very specific, such as making oxygen in Unit 1.4 or identifying food chains in Unit 3.4. However, in the outside world, many investigations start with a vague idea or question, such as how the Solar System was formed, or how we can make a better washing machine.

School science is similar to science in the outside world. Many school science investigations are also directly related to jobs people do in life outside school. For example, in school you may investigate stars in space such as the Cassiopeia constellation (see Figure 1), using the Faulkes telescope. Astronomers at Queen's University or Armagh Observatory investigate the Universe using telescopes in the Canary Islands, Chile and Armagh.

activity Mini challenge

Figure 3 Testing a new exhaust gas catalyst for a car.

Using the school library and appropriate websites, in a small group, identify an investigation you have done recently, and find out how it is similar to an outside world activity. If your recent investigation involved recycling carbon dioxide (see Unit 3.5), then the 'outside world' activity might be in an aircraft company or a university research laboratory trying to reduce the amount of carbon dioxide emitted by engines (see Figure 3). You can get information from appropriate websites.

Then, having agreed responsibilities within your group, find out who uses the science or technology related to your recent investigation, possibly using the careers pages on **www.W5online.co.uk**. This provides information on, for example, the work of astronomers and aerospace engineers. Finally, present an illustrated report (for a school audience) showing how your school investigation is linked to scientific or industrial applications, and on possible jobs or careers in one of the applications you have discovered.

You can use activity sheet
X13 Meeting the challenge to
help you with some of this.

Although these activities will vary with the nature of the challenge, here is a possible sequence.

1 Identify the issues involved in your challenge. How do you investigate the formation of the Solar System, or how an aeroplane engine is made? What <u>specific</u> questions do you want to answer?

2 Develop possible outcomes, and decide on a sense of direction. What do you want to produce at the end of the activity? How do you intend to get there?

3 How do you share the responsibilities within your group? What help do you need from outside (scientists, engineers, teachers and others)? Who does what? What material resources do you need?

4 Make appropriate observations and measurements, and research answers to questions.

5 Come to conclusions, and evaluate these. What are your observations, measurements and detailed conclusions? What general conclusions can you draw? What went well? What could have been done better?

6 Relate the activity to the outside world (including social, commercial and environmental implications) and career opportunities, for example what do astronomers or aerospace engineers do all day? How can you become one?

7 Present a report using the most effective means. Who is your audience? What is the best way of presenting your findings to this audience?

Your report can be presented in one or more of the following formats:
- a written report for a school magazine/newspaper, with pictures
- a poster presentation (possibly with models)
- an electronic presentation
- pages on a website.

Your report should include:
- a short description of the investigation and its scientific application
- a list of the skills and understanding you developed in your own investigation
- how these skills and understanding relate to the 'outside world' scientific or engineering application
- how these skills and understanding relate to a possible job or career in science or technology
- how you would go about taking up this career.

---

activity Current science issue

Choose a science issue currently in the news. Follow the sequence above to refine your enquiry, and present a final report in one of the formats in Step 7.

4 Food and digestion

→ 4.1 What are you putting in your mouth?

> ### → In this unit we are learning:
> - about the seven nutrients necessary for good health
> - to make healthy food choices (personal health)
> - that people and the media can influence food choices (citizenship/media awareness)
> - about the work of dieticians (employability).

Figure 1 Did you know: most soft drinks contain as much sugar as two or three lollipops, or two packets of sweets?

Look back to Unit 3.1 on page 41 to see what elements are in your body.

Seven nutrients

You have already learned in Chapter 1 that everything is made from a combination of elements. This means that your body and the food that you eat are a mixture of different elements too, sometimes combined into compounds like sugar or butter. You have heard people saying 'You are what you eat'. However, people are sometimes unaware that some of the food they are eating is not good for their health.

Foods contain different amounts of seven **nutrients**. Nutrients are substances that take part in the chemical reactions of the body, or are necessary for **good health**. The seven nutrients are **carbohydrates, fats, proteins, vitamins, minerals, fibre** and **water**. Each nutrient performs a different role in the body. It is important that you eat the correct balance of these seven nutrients. This is known as a healthy **balanced diet**.

Nutrient	Food	Uses
carbohydrates	sugar and starchy foods	provides energy
fats	butter and oily foods	for insulation, and a source of energy
proteins	baked beans, red meat and eggs	for growth and repair
vitamin A	eggs	for vision
vitamin C	citrus fruits	for healthy gums and blood vessels
vitamin D	milk	for healthy bones and teeth
minerals: iron	red meat	for red blood cells
minerals: calcium	milk	makes bones and teeth strong
fibre	fruit and vegetables and wholegrain foods	prevents constipation
water	drinking water	for cell support and for making blood

Table 1 Nutrients in food and their uses.

red meat, fats and starches
examples: burgers, sausages (red meat),
butter (fats), pasta, bread (starches)

dairy products
examples: milk, ice-cream, cream

fish, poultry, eggs

fruit and vegetables
examples: lettuce, oranges, apples, broccoli, cabbage

wholegrain foods
examples: cereals such as bran, wholemeal bread

Figure 2 Foods that are good sources of a particular nutrient are often arranged into food groups, as shown by this food pyramid. A healthy diet will include more foods from the lower levels and fewer foods from the higher levels.

activity ## Foods for a healthy balanced diet

Be safe: You must not eat any of the foods used in this activity

In this activity we will examine the seven nutrients and their roles in the body. Your teacher may give you, or you may make, three sets of cards. One set has the names of each of the different nutrient groups, one set has a picture of a particular nutrient, and a third set has the function of the nutrient in the body.

1 Working with a partner, sort and match examples of the seven nutrients with their pictures and functions. Decide how to organise your results. Use a stop clock to time how long it takes you. At the end check the correct answers with your teacher. Add 5 seconds for each set of cards you have matched incorrectly.

2 Now locate the positions of the following foods on the food pyramid shown in Figure 2: bread, butter, cabbage, bran. Measure out 20 g of each of the four foods.

3 Do you notice any difference between the amounts of each food type? Write sentences to compare the amounts of foods with the same mass.

4 Place the foods in order starting with the type of food you think you could eat more of before you would feel 'full up'. Is there a pattern between the amount of food you think you could eat most of and its position in the food pyramid?

5 Use your results to suggest a reason why people who eat more high-fat, take-away foods feel hungry again after a short time.

6 Use books or the internet to research the topic of 'Healthy eating' to help you to produce a leaflet for upper primary pupils that gives ten tips for healthy eating. You should try to illustrate your work.

7 Create a spray diagram for the seven main nutrients, examples of each nutrient and the role they have in your body.

activity Nutrients mnemonic

You remember from Year 8 that a **mnemonic** is a technique used to help you remember facts, where the first letter of a fact is replaced by a common word. Design a mnemonic to help you to remember the names of the nutrients.

activity Dietician

1 Search books or the internet to find out about the work of a dietician.
2 In a small group, prepare an electronic presentation to show what a dietician does, and how dieticians help us.

Figure 3 Dietician at work.

extension activity Wartime diet

Search books or the internet to find out about food rationing that was introduced in the Second World War. What did food rationing mean? What foods were not available? What did people use to replace these foods? Suggest three reasons why this diet is thought to be better for our health than the high-fat diet that is popular in society today.

Eating habits

Many pupils obtain their main meal of the day from the school canteen. In 2005 a celebrity chef launched a campaign to increase the range of healthy food options offered in school canteens. The power of public opinion forced the government to take action to change the choice of food on offer in school canteens. Many schools also banned the sale of fizzy drinks, sweets and crisps.

activity

Good foods and bad foods?

This activity asks you to look more closely at the foods that you are eating. You are asked to identify what you consider to be 'bad' foods. However, you may find that these foods would not badly affect your health if eaten as part of a balanced diet.

1   As a class, create a list of questions you could use to decide whether particular foods are 'bad foods' or 'good foods'. Some suggestions include: high fat content, salt content.

2   Create your own list of ten foods you consider are 'bad foods' and ten 'good foods'. Give reasons to support your suggestions for either list.

3   Make a personal food chart for the foods you eat on a typical day. How many of the foods on your list do you consider are 'bad foods' and how many are 'good foods'? Try to suggest better foods than the 'bad' food choices that you made.

4   The aim of the campaign in 2005 was to ban **junk food** from school canteens. Try to find a definition for the term 'junk food'.

5   Some of the effects of junk food on children include: a lack of energy, mood swings, hyperactivity, poor concentration, obesity and constipation. Find out more about each of these conditions.

6   What effect would you expect from eating large amounts of junk food on your ability to learn?

7   Make a list of reasons for and against the sale of only healthy snacks in your school.

8   Working in a small group, write a letter to your principal to highlight why sugary drinks and snacks should not be sold in school. Try to support your campaign by reporting the effects that eating too much sugar can have on health.

Figure 4 Is this a healthy choice?

1   **Find a definition for each of the terms 'starvation' and 'malnutrition', and explain the difference between them.**

2   **Suggest two reasons why people do not always make healthy food choices.**

3   **Suggest some groups of people likely to be in favour of the policy of banning 'junk food'. Suggest a reason for each group of people that you identify.**

→ 4.2 The Peppermint poisoning

→ **In this unit we are learning:**

- to develop practical skills in using equipment
- to investigate the nutrients present in food
- to draw conclusions from an investigation.

Most foods are mixtures of the seven nutrients described in the previous unit, but some foods are a good source of only one nutrient. There are several tests using **reagents** for identifying whether a food contains a particular nutrient. The names of the food tests, instructions for carrying out each test, and how to identify whether or not the nutrient is present are given in Figure 1.

test for carbohydrates

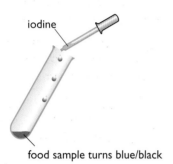

iodine

food sample turns blue/black

test for fat

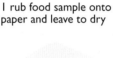

1 rub food sample onto paper and leave to dry

2 translucent stain appears round sample when held up to the light

test for glucose

Benedict's solution

food sample turns orange/red

heat

test for protein (Biuret test)

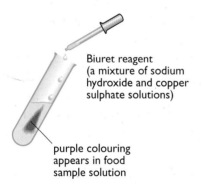

Biuret reagent (a mixture of sodium hydroxide and copper sulphate solutions)

purple colouring appears in food sample solution

Figure 1 Food tests.

1 **Name a food that would change the colour of iodine from brown to blue.**

2 **What is the name of the reagent used to test for protein?**

3 **When testing for starch what colour change shows starch is present in the food being tested?**

4 **a What reagent is used to test for sugar?**
 b What is the starting colour of this reagent?
 c What colour does it become if there is sugar in the food tested?

5 **Jack knows that cheese is a good source of protein. Helen thinks cheese is a high-fat food. Suggest how they could settle their argument.**

6 **Jan tested some sweets using Biuret reagent. Suggest the colour of the reagent at the end of the test. Explain your answer.**

7 **When performing the starch test, Robin accidentally spilt some reagent onto the pages of her workbook. The reagent changed colour to blue-black.**
 – **Name the reagent Robin was using to perform the test.**
 – **State the colour change that she observed.**
 – **Suggest a reason to explain why the reagent changed colour.**

Investigation   The body in the bedroom

In this activity you will develop the skills for performing the four food tests. Your teacher may use this activity to assess your practical skills. Read the passage below and follow the instructions carefully.

Be safe: You must not taste any of the food samples

Lady Lilac invited a party of eight guests to stay for a few days. On the first night the party dined at eight o'clock. After dinner, however, Mrs Peppermint felt ill. Making her apologies, she went to her room for the night while the other guests partied on until midnight. It was only when Mr Peppermint went to his room that he discovered the dead body of his poor wife.

During a post-mortem examination it was discovered that the stomach contents of Mrs Peppermint contained poison. Further analysis showed that the poison was rich in protein.

Figure 2 Lady Lilac and her guests at dinner.

Figure 3 Mr Peppermint discovers the body of his dead wife.

You have been recruited as part of a team of forensic scientists to investigate the source of the poison. You will be given four different liquids that could contain starch, sugar, fat or protein. You must identify the main nutrient present in each of the four samples. You should then be able to identify which liquid is the source of the poison.

1 Work in a small group. Figure 1 gives you instructions for performing each food test. Read through the instructions for each test carefully.

2 You must do the four food tests on each of the four samples to find out which one is the source of the poison. <u>Before starting the experiment,</u> decide in your group the order in which you will carry out each of the tests. Do you think it is a good idea for everyone to do each of the tests? Will you perform each test in turn or start them all at the same time? After five minutes you will find out the ideas of the other groups in the class.

3 When you are told to do so, perform the food tests and record your results.

4 For each food test in turn, explain how you know whether the test is positive or not. Also decide how you should record the results for each test.

5 Now decide which of the four samples is the source of the poison.

6 Discuss with the other members of your group whether you could write new methods for the food tests that you would find easier to follow. Remember to write a list of safety rules that you will apply in each of the tests.

→ 4.3 How can we work safely in a laboratory, and carry out a risk assessment?

→ **In this unit we are learning:**

- to understand the meanings of *hazard* and *risk*, and the difference between them (personal health)
- to carry out a risk assessment (citizenship).

Figure 1 The hazard symbol.

In Unit 4.2 there is a hazard symbol, and you are told to *Be safe: You must not taste any of the food samples.* Several other units in this book have hazard symbols, and other instructions like *Be safe: You must wear eye protection.* These instructions are designed to ensure that you work safely in the laboratory: that **risks** from **hazards** like poisonous substances or splashing chemicals are kept as low as possible.

A hazard is defined by the Health and Safety Executive in Northern Ireland (HSENI) to be anything which can cause harm, e.g. chemicals, electricity, working at a height, poor lighting, etc. The risk is the chance or likelihood that someone will be harmed to some extent by the hazard.

For example when you are crossing a busy road, the *hazard* is that you will be hit by a car. If you act sensibly and make sure nothing is coming, the *risk* of you being hit is very low. However, if you simply rush into the road without looking the *risk* that you can be seriously injured or killed can be very high.

Before people begin to do anything that might be hazardous, for example a teacher taking pupils to a farm, or a decorator painting a high ceiling, they are expected to carry out a **risk assessment.** In this they follow five steps identified by the HSE to make workplaces (including schools) safer to work in.

1 Identify the hazards.
2 Decide who might be harmed and how.
3 Assess the risks and decide on precautions.
4 Record findings and implement them.
5 Review assessment and update if necessary.

Figure 2 What are the risks in these scenes?

activity   Identifying hazards

You have just done an investigation into testing food samples for specific nutrients. With a partner, read the activity: *The body in the bedroom* again, and the notes you made on it. Then:

a list the possible hazards
b decide the precautions you would take to avoid possible injury to yourself or other people around you.

Say whether the risk is low, medium or high. You can use activity sheet *X14 Risk assessment* to help you carry out this risk assessment.

1 Explain the difference between the terms: 'hazard' and 'risk'.

2 Why is it essential for a scientist to carry out a risk assessment before he/she starts work on laboratory experiments, such as examining bacteria or varying the pressure inside glass equipment?

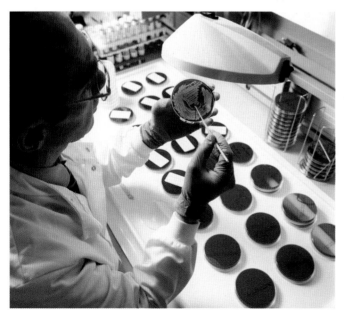

Figure 3 a Bacterial research.   b Using glass equipment in chemical research.

→ 4.4 Energy!

→ **In this unit we are learning:**

- to plan an experiment
- to measure the energy content in foods
- to examine how the media present information (media awareness)
- about problems of poor diet (personal health).

Figure 1 Energy drinks.

Nutrition

A serving (75g) when cooked weighs approximately 170g.

Typical Composition	A serving (75g) when cooked contains	100g contain
Energy	1130kJ 270kcal	1510kJ 355kcal
Protein	9.4g	12.5g
Carbohydrate	54.8g	73.0g
of which sugars	1.8g	2.4g
Fat	1.1g	1.4g
of which saturates	0.2g	0.3g
Fibre	2.0g	2.6g
Sodium	trace	trace

A serving (75g) when cooked contains the equivalent of trace salt.

Figure 2 Nutritional information on a bag of pasta.

Food for energy

Your body uses energy all the time. Your heart uses energy to pump blood around your body, your brain uses energy to think and learn, and your muscles use energy during active sports. You get this energy from food and drink. Energy is released by a chemical reaction called **respiration** that you learned about last year:

fuel + oxygen → carbon dioxide + water + energy

In our bodies, the fuel for this reaction is food. You will learn more about respiration in Chapter 7.

The amount of energy you need depends on factors such as your age, sex and lifestyle. Energy is recorded in units called **joules** (J), which you met last year. There are one thousand joules in one **kilojoule** (kJ).

Manufacturers state the amount of energy that a food can provide on the wrapper. (See Figure 2.) This is normally given as the amount of energy in 100 g of the food. Often two values are given for energy: in kilojoules and in kilocalories. The kilojoule is the metric value. However, some people are more familiar with an older unit, the kilocalorie. One **kilocalorie** equals about 4.2 kilojoules or 4200 joules.

Figure 3 Some foods are packaged as 'low calorie' snacks. Others keep the calories under wraps!

Figure 4 Some crisps are marketed as 'low-fat' varieties.

activity Food on the go

Figure 5 What do you think?

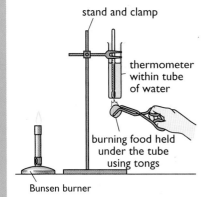

stand and clamp

thermometer within tube of water

burning food held under the tube using tongs

Bunsen burner

Figure 6 Measuring the energy content in food.

In this activity you will examine the amount of energy that different types of crisp provide.

You can find out the amount of energy in a food when it is set alight. The heat energy that is released is used to heat a tube of water. Foods with more energy produce more heat.

1 Working with a partner, plan an experiment that will allow you to help Jim and his friends to settle their argument. Remember to plan a fair test and to include safety rules. Show your teacher your plan.
2 Your teacher will demonstrate this experiment for you.
3 What did you find out? Write a sentence to describe your results.
4 Do you think this is an accurate way to measure the energy content in food? Explain your answer.

extension activity Comparing energy and fat

1 Collect the labels from some foods and drinks. You could choose some of the following examples: shortbread, butter, chocolate, crisps, nuts, cereal, yoghurt, cheese, lemonade, bread, apples, milk.
2 Examine the labels and record how much energy is available from 100 g of each product (100 ml for liquids). Make sure you record this value, as some labels quote the energy content of the whole product itself rather than per 100 g. Also record the amount of fat that each food contains.
3 Compare the amount of energy and the amount of fat recorded for each food. Can you spot a pattern between the amounts of energy and fat in each product? Write a sentence to describe this pattern.

It is important that the amount of energy you obtain from your diet equals the energy your body uses daily, otherwise conditions like **obesity** might occur. Obesity is a condition caused when extra energy from the diet is changed into fat and is stored around your body. The Department of Health in Northern Ireland is worried by the number of people who are obese. Every year millions of people die from illnesses that develop from people being obese, such as heart disease and diabetes. Obesity is often a concern for teenagers who even risk their health in their attempts to avoid becoming obese. This is shown by the media article on page 71.

 activity

Dieting by avoiding dairy foods?

This activity asks you to look at how the media present scientific information. The article 'The teenagers 'allergic' to a healthy diet' appeared in a national newspaper. Read the article carefully and answer the following questions.

1　Do you think the title of the article is appropriate? Explain your answer. Suggest a more suitable title.
2　Why do you think the Milk Development Council conducted this poll of young people?
3　Do you think the view presented by the article is accurate? Do you think it could be biased? Give reasons to support your answers.
4　Who else would you need to interview to decide whether or not the article is accurate? Write a list of five questions you would ask them.
5　Suggest three reasons why teenage girls want to look like stars such as Madonna.
6　Why might young children imagine dairy products are fattening?
7　Many primary schools offer a small bottle of milk to their pupils at break-time. Do you think this policy is a good idea? Give two reasons to support your answer.
8　Find out more about the benefits of dairy products to health. Design a leaflet to promote these products to teenagers.

Figure 7 Is a bottle of milk at break-time a good idea?

The teenagers 'allergic' to a healthy diet

Teenage girls are risking their health by avoiding milk, cheese and yoghurt to copy skinny stars. One in ten aged 11 to 16 claims to be allergic to dairy food because they fear it will make them fat, a poll has found. In reality only one in 25 has a medically diagnosed food allergy. In the survey, 47 per cent said they had been on a diet or wanted to go on one, 40 per cent felt under pressure to look like super-slim stars such as Victoria Beckham and Madonna. Dairy food was seen as fattening and 40 per cent of girls tried to avoid it.

The Milk Development Council, who commissioned the poll, said adolescents who cut out dairy products risked long-term health consequences. It said only one-quarter of girls in their early teens eats enough dairy food for the calcium they need to protect them against osteoporosis. 'The fact that girls think milk is fattening and are self-diagnosing food allergies is alarming'.

Daily Mail, Saturday 6 May 2006

---

activity   Osteoporosis

Osteoporosis is mentioned in the newspaper article. This is a condition that can develop from not getting enough calcium from your diet. Find out more about osteoporosis by searching books or the internet for information. Questions you should answer include these.

- What are the causes of osteoporosis?
- Who is likely to be most at risk from the disease?
- How can the risk of the disease be reduced?

---

1 **Explain how obesity is caused.**
2 **Suggest why having an active lifestyle can help to avoid developing obesity.**
3 a **Suggest why people today are more likely to eat convenience foods than in previous years.**
  b **Suggest why food manufacturers must state the nutrients that are present in the foods they make.**
4 **People who regularly eat large amounts of fast food, which is usually high in fat, are more likely to become obese. Can you suggest a reason for this?**

→ 4.5 Break it down!

→ **In this unit we are learning:**

- to understand how enzymes help in the digestion of food
- to investigate enzyme action.

Have you ever wondered what happens to your food after it is swallowed? When you swallow, muscles push the food downwards – although they will push it upwards if you eat while standing on your head! The actions of these muscles mix food with natural chemicals called **enzymes**.

Investigation Mixing and grinding

This activity should help you understand the effects of physical digestion in the breakdown of food. You will use a special type of material called **Visking tubing** (or dialysis tubing). This material has holes that allow only tiny molecules such as sugar and water to pass through it. It is similar to the leaky walls of your gut.

1 Measure two 15 cm lengths of Visking tubing. Seal one end of each by twisting it into a knot and secure this tightly using a small new paperclip. Support the two tubes as shown in Figure 1.

2 Roughly crumble half a plain biscuit and weigh a 5 g portion. Add this to one of the Visking tubes using a spatula.

3 Using a pestle and mortar, thoroughly crush the other half of the plain biscuit and weigh a 5 g portion. Add this to the second tube using a spatula.

4 Add some food dye to water. Measure 10 ml of this liquid and add it to the first Visking tube, securing the open end with a paper clip. Add a second 10 ml to the second Visking tube, securing the open end with a paper clip. Leave both tubes undisturbed for a few minutes then examine each of the tubes.

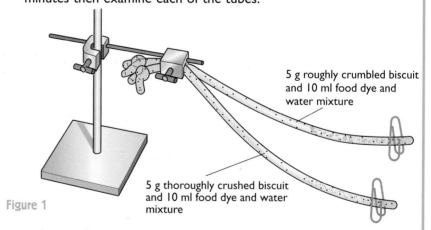

5 g roughly crumbled biscuit and 10 ml food dye and water mixture

5 g thoroughly crushed biscuit and 10 ml food dye and water mixture

Figure 1

5 Compare the two tubes. Write a sentence to describe each of them. Write a sentence to describe how they are different from each other.

6 Which tube do you think represents the result of physical digestion? Explain your answer.

Figure 2 Ivan Pavlov.

Chemical digestion

When food enters your mouth, a liquid called **saliva** is added, and acts to lubricate the movement of food down your throat. This is one of many liquids, known as **secretions,** that are released into your mouth and gut. The secretion of saliva, even at the thought of food, was investigated by the Russian scientist, Ivan Pavlov (1849–1936). In 1904 he received the Nobel Prize in Physiology or Medicine, for his studies on how the digestive system works.

extension activity Pavlov's dog

You might have heard of 'Pavlov's dog'. Search books and the internet to find out more about Pavlov's work, and why his dog was important.

Enzyme action

Other secretions that are released into the gut include hydrochloric acid, gastric juice and intestinal juice. Some of these secretions contain enzymes. Enzymes help to break down the larger nutrients present in food, which are carbohydrates, fats and proteins. There is a different type of enzyme for each of these nutrients.

Investigation What do enzymes do?

In this activity you will examine the effect of enzymes. You will use liquid biological and non-biological detergents. The biological liquid contains enzymes that have similar actions to the enzymes that are released in your gut.

Be safe: Liquid detergents may cause skin irritation

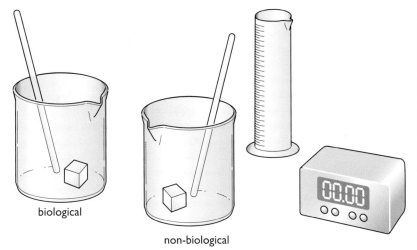

biological

non-biological

Figure 3

1 Cut two 2 cm × 2 cm × 2 cm cubes of gelatine.
2 Place one cube into each of two small beakers. Label one beaker 'biological' and the other 'non-biological'.
3 Using a cylinder, measure 25 ml of a biological liquid detergent and add to the labelled beaker.

4 Measure a second 25 ml of non-biological liquid detergent and add to the second beaker.

5 Start a timer and, using a stirring rod, stir the liquid in each beaker for five minutes. Do not attempt to break up the cube of gelatine with the rod. Try to stir each liquid at the same rate.

6 After five minutes of stirring, pour out the contents of each beaker and examine the size of the pieces of gelatine that remain.

7 Write a few sentences to describe and compare the effect that each detergent had on the pieces of gelatine.

8 The gelatine that you used in this experiment is a protein. Use this piece of information to try to explain your results.

9 Find out more about the difference between biological and non-biological washing liquids. Find out the cost of similar brands of these types of liquids. Which of the two types provides best value for money? How did you decide?

Investigation

Be safe: You must wear eye protection. Be careful when using a knife

Investigating enzyme action

Enzymes work best at a particular pH value. An enzyme called tyrosinase is present in apples and makes the flesh of the apple turn brown when it is in the air. It is your task to plan an investigation to examine how pH affects the activity of tyrosinase enzyme in turning apples brown.

You are supplied with the following materials: a Granny Smith apple, universal indicator, lemon juice (acid pH), water (neutral pH), baking soda solution (alkaline pH), beakers, white tile, a knife, and a timer.

You must write a list of instructions that will allow you to find out what effect each solution has on the browning of apples. You will need to know the pH of each solution and be able to record results. Remember to make your experiment safe and to plan a fair test. Show your plans to your teacher before beginning the experiment.

---

1 **Write definitions for the terms 'enzymes' and 'secretions'.**

2 **Does your mouth start to water just by looking at certain foods? Make a list of these foods. Compare your list with a partner. Do you have common foods?**

4.6 On a food journey

Look back at Unit 3.5 and add to your story about the journey of a carbon atom through time.

The seven nutrients described in Unit 4.1 must enter your body cells, where they can take part in chemical reactions vital for life, such as respiration (see Chapter 7). Cells are tiny, so food needs to be broken up into tiny pieces to enter your cells. This happens by a process called **digestion**, which is the breakdown of large insoluble food pieces into smaller soluble pieces. Figure 1 shows the structures of the parts of the digestive system, which is sometimes called the **gut**. If you study the gut carefully you will notice it is a long, continuous muscular tube that stretches from the mouth to the **anus**.

With your finger, trace the pathway of food from the mouth to the small intestine, where nutrients are small enough to enter the bloodstream. In the **small intestine** a process called **absorption** occurs. The nutrients travel across the walls of the small intestine, which acts like a sponge and soaks up the small nutrients.

When your body digests carbohydrates, **glucose**, a sugar, is produced. Glucose is carried in the bloodstream to the liver, where it is stored until it is needed for respiration. Other small nutrients travel to the body cells and are used in chemical reactions. Insoluble material and water travel onwards to the **large intestine**, where water is removed. Any wastes and undigested food are removed from the body through the rectum and finally, the **anus**.

Along the gut are muscles that help to move food along. This process is known as **peristalsis**. Peristalsis in the large intestine helps to prevent **constipation**. Your teacher will tell you where to find websites with more information about peristalsis in fun format. (Why do we vomit?)

Your teacher will give you a website where you can observe the digestive system in action (on-line tour of the digestive system), and take the digestive health quiz.

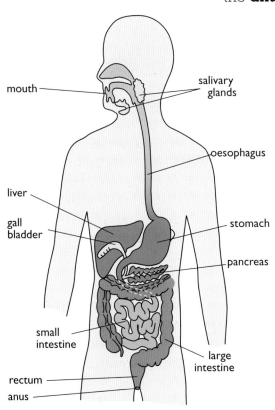

mouth

salivary glands

oesophagus

liver

gall bladder

stomach

pancreas

small intestine

large intestine

rectum

anus

Figure 1 The digestive system.

---

extension activity — I'm going to be sick

Find out why it is difficult to vomit, and why vomiting is sometimes called 'reverse peristalsis'.

extension activity

Moving through the digestive system

In this activity you are asked to examine the events that occur at each step in the digestive system.

1 The steps that take place as food passes through the gut are listed below in random order. Using the picture of the gut in Figure 1, place the statements in the correct order.

Figure 2 Digestion circle.

A Soluble food leaves the gut and enters the bloodstream.
B Food passes down the oesophagus to the stomach.
C Undigested food waste passes through this ring of muscle.
D Food enters the mouth where it is chewed and mixed with saliva.
E Food passes by the liver and pancreas, which release bile and digestive enzymes.
F Food is stored for a short time and is mixed with gastric juice, and acid.
G Water is removed from food and enters the bloodstream.
H Undigested food waste collects here for a short time.

2 You should have identified statement D as the first step. This is already placed into the first segment on the diagram of the digestion circle (see Figure 2). Copy the circle in your workbook. Write the statements in their correct order in the blank spaces.
3 Create a spray diagram as a summary for the structures of the digestive system and their functions.

activity

Digestive system

Your teacher will divide the members of the class so that each group will be asked to research one part of the digestive system. Search the internet to observe each of the structures of the digestive system in more detail. Record any additional information you find about your chosen structure. Decide how you will record this information. Try to make the information interesting for other members of your class. All pieces of information should be brought together and displayed for everyone in the class to record.

Where does food go to after digestion?

Some foods, such as fibre-rich foods like sweetcorn shells and bran, cannot be digested by enzymes. These foods are too large to be able to pass through the walls of the small intestine to enter the blood stream. Instead they travel onwards in liquids, mainly water, to the large intestine. As most of the water is removed in the large intestine a semi-solid waste material called **faeces** is produced that eventually passes out of the body through the anus. If it did not contain some water, faeces could not continue on its journey along the large intestine. This can cause a condition called constipation. Doctors recommend that if you eat a lot of fibre you should drink a lot of liquid. This is shown in the activity below.

practical activity A good fibre provider?

Fibre-rich foods can often soak up or absorb liquid. To ensure that food continues to move through the gut, water is needed. More water is absorbed by some fibre-rich foods than others. You will be given two cereals A and B. In this activity it is your task to identify which cereal absorbs more water quickly.

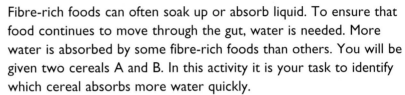

filter paper and funnel

cereal

timer

measuring cylinder

water collected

Figure 3

1 Use a balance to weigh out 10 g of each type of cereal.
2 Crush each cereal using a pestle and mortar for one minute. Then place each cereal into 100 ml beakers.
3 Measure 50 ml of water twice and add 50 ml to each beaker at the same time. Give each beaker a quick stir using a stirring rod and start a timer.
4 Leave each beaker undisturbed for 5 minutes.
5 After 5 minutes, carefully filter the contents of each beaker. Make sure you scrape all of the cereal and liquid into the funnel.
6 Leave each filter to drip for 10 minutes. Record how much water has collected in each cylinder.
7 Now, do the following.
   a Work out how much water was soaked up by each cereal.
   b State which cereal soaked up more liquid.
   c Write a sentence to describe the results that you obtained for each cereal.
   d Which cereal do you think is more likely to cause constipation? Explain your answer.
   e State the ways you made the experiment a fair test.

extension activity Fibre comparison

For many people cereals provide a source of fibre in the diet. Many people eat cornflakes. Search the internet or books to find out how cornflakes were discovered (try entering 'W K Kellogg' in a search engine). Compare the amount of fibre that is present in at least five popular breakfast cereals such as oats, maize, bran, etc.

1 **Suggest a reason why people eating a high-fibre diet should drink plenty of liquids.**
2 **Imagine you have just put a sugary sweet into your mouth. List in order the structures of the gut that it would travel through. Explain why the sweet would look very different to when you first ate it.**

Compounds and mixtures

→ ## 5.1 Element or compound: can you spot the difference?

→ **In this unit we are learning:**

- to sort substances into elements and compounds
- to interpret chemical formulae, and relate the numbers to the numbers of atoms involved
- to understand the idea of energy change during compound formation
- to describe the formation of iron sulphide from its elements: iron and sulphur.

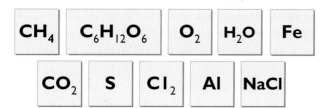

Figure 1 Formula cards.

In Chapter 1 we learned that an element is a substance that is made up of just one kind of atom, and that a compound is made up of two or more elements chemically joined together. We discovered that it was very difficult to separate the elements in a compound.

activity Sorting picture cards of common substances

Look at Figure 1 and Figure 3, and sort the substances into elements and compounds.

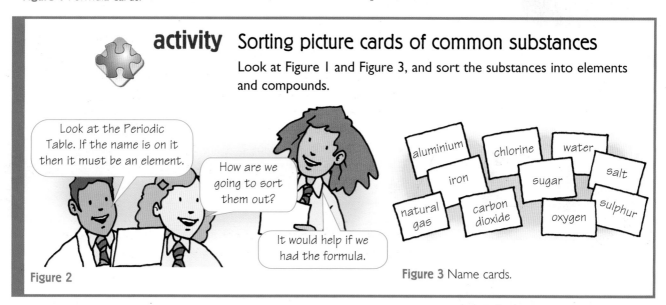

Figure 2

Figure 3 Name cards.

The formula tells us how many different elements are in the substance. If all the atoms are the same then it must be an element. The numbers also tell us how many atoms of each element there are in the substance.

activity Making a compound from iron and sulphur

Be safe: You must wear eye protection

Figure 4 Iron filings and sulphur powder.

You need the following apparatus: boiling tube, test tube holder, Bunsen burner, heatproof mat, eye protection, magnet. You also need chemicals: iron filings and powdered sulphur.

1 Watch your teacher do the experiment and then you may try it yourself.
2 Mix some iron filings with sulphur powder on a piece of white paper. Use a magnet to remove the iron filings leaving the yellow sulphur powder.
3 Mix the iron and sulphur again and then put the mixture into a boiling tube. Carefully heat the boiling tube in a Bunsen flame, watching for any colour changes.
4 When a red glow appears inside the tube, remove it from the flame. Keep watching the colour of the contents of the tube. When the colour fades put the boiling tube onto the heatproof mat and leave it to cool.
5 Record your observations.

Figure 5 Iron reacting with sulphur.

I think it was the glass glowing.

It must have been a very hot flame.

Maybe the chemicals were producing extra heat energy.

Figure 6 What do you think?

Did you see the red glow getting brighter even after the tube had been taken out of the flame? When a compound is formed, an energy change takes place. In this reaction heat energy is given out to the surroundings, and that is why the compound glows even after it has been taken away from the Bunsen flame.

The solid which forms is a black colour, different from the grey iron filings. Do you think you will be able to separate the iron from the sulphur now? Try using a magnet to find out. What should the new substance be called? Can you write a chemical formula for this new compound?

The ratio of iron to sulphur in this compound is 50:50. This means that for every atom of iron there is one of sulphur. The formula is FeS. The name of the compound is iron sulphide.

---

1 **How many different elements are there in each of the following compounds? Name the elements in each compound.**

$C_6H_{12}O_6$ Al_2O_3 $CuSO_4$ Na_2CO_3 $FeCl_2$

2 **Draw a diagram of the apparatus you used in the iron sulphide experiment.**
3 **How did you know that an energy change was taking place?**
4 **Why is it difficult to separate the iron and sulphur in iron sulphide?**

→ 5.2 Why is the dome of Belfast City Hall green?

→ **In this unit we are learning that:**

- elements can react with the substances around them
- metals often react with elements in the air to form compounds
- metallic elements are often used to make buildings look attractive
- thermal decomposition means to break down a compound using heat energy.

Figure 2 A new two pence coin, showing the pinkish brown copper. The coin will gradually turn dull and may even turn green at the edges.

Figure 3 Green copper carbonate powder.

Figure 4 A Rag Day stunt.

Belfast City Hall was built just over 100 years ago. The dome is 53 metres tall, and is coated in copper metal. Copper is a pinkish brown metal with a shiny surface.

Why is the dome of the City Hall green? Copper is a metallic element which was used to coat the dome to make the building look very grand. When it was newly built the dome would have been very shiny, and it would have had the pinkish brown colour of the copper metal.

Figure 1 Belfast City Hall, with its green dome.

Over the years the dome has been exposed to the air and to all weather conditions. When copper reacts with the air, it combines with both the moisture and the carbon dioxide in the air to form a compound called basic copper carbonate, which is green in colour. It is a form of atmospheric corrosion.

As the time passes, this coating of copper carbonate covers the copper and the dome appears to be green. The layer of copper carbonate, becomes thicker as the building gets older. We are used to seeing it as a green dome.

Queen's University in Belfast has a day each year called Rag Day. On this day the students do unusual things to attract attention, and raise as much money as possible for charities.

On one Rag Day in the 1960s students managed to write the letters PTQ (the title of their rag magazine) on the dome of the City Hall in black paint. Removing the paint was an expensive job. To clean it completely, they would have had to remove all the copper carbonate, so they could only clean the patches in the centre. This left three patches which were a different colour to the rest of the dome and they looked dirty. Those patches are still a slightly different colour to the rest of the dome.

extension activity   Metal decoration

Use the internet to find out more about buildings with copper domes. Are any other metals used to make buildings look attractive?

The word equation for the reaction of copper with water and carbon dioxide is:

copper + water + carbon dioxide → copper carbonate

Copper carbonate occurs naturally in a rock called malachite. It is a bright green compound which is insoluble in water, and was used as a green pigment in artists' colours.

Figure 5 Carbon dioxide is released when copper carbonate is heated.

Investigation   Heating copper carbonate

Be safe: You must wear eye protection. Be careful to remove the test tube containing limewater before removing the Bunsen flame to avoid suck back

You need the following apparatus: boiling tube, retort stand and clamp, rubber bung with delivery tube, test tube, spatula, eye protection, Bunsen burner. You also need chemicals: copper carbonate powder and limewater.

1 Set up the apparatus as shown in Figure 5.
2 Carefully heat the copper carbonate with a medium Bunsen flame.
3 Watch carefully for any colour changes.
4 Write a report of your experiment in your notebook.

The copper carbonate was broken down by the heat to form two new substances. One of these was a black powder called copper oxide. The other product was carbon dioxide gas. This gas turns limewater from colourless to milky white. This is the test for carbon dioxide. When heat energy is used to break down a compound, we say that **thermal decomposition** has taken place.

The word equation for this reaction is:

copper carbonate → copper oxide + carbon dioxide

1 **Why was copper chosen to make the dome of the City Hall in Belfast?**
2 **What substances did the copper react with to make it turn green?**
3 **Write a word equation for the reaction of copper with water and carbon dioxide.**
4 **How did you make copper oxide from copper carbonate?**
5 **What is meant by 'thermal decomposition'?**

→ 5.3 How do compounds react with each other?

→ **In this unit we are learning:**

■ to decide whether a chemical reaction has taken place
■ to recognise that reactions can take place between compounds
■ to explain observations in terms of reacting particles.

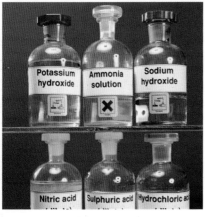

Figure 1 Bottles of common chemicals.

Look at the picture of some chemical compounds found in most school laboratories. Compounds are formed when elements join together. We are going to investigate whether compounds can react with each other.

I've got a reaction!

Figure 2

---

practical activity

You must wear eye protection. Do not taste any of the chemicals. Do not put your fingers into your mouth when handling liquids. Wash your hands after the experiment

Mixing chemical compounds

You need the following apparatus: test tube rack with clean dry test tubes, small beakers, cloth to wipe up spills, spatula, watchglass. You also need chemicals: sodium carbonate solution, dilute hydrochloric acid, iron II chloride solution, ammonia solution, copper sulphate solution, solid magnesium carbonate. Your teacher will provide you with the chemicals in labelled beakers.

1 Pour about 5 cm³ of iron II chloride solution into a test tube. Note the colour and appearance of this compound.
2 Add an equal amount of sodium carbonate solution. Watch to see if you think there is a reaction.
3 Repeat this procedure again with the following:
    – ammonia solution added to copper sulphate solution
    – magnesium carbonate powder added to dilute hydrochloric acid.
4 Design and complete a table for your results.

Did you see those bubbles?

Wow! look at that – it looks like a jelly fish.

That's amazing!

Figure 3 Discussing a reaction.

Figure 4 Apparatus for making paint activity.

How do we decide if a reaction has taken place? Sometimes there is a change in colour. Sometimes a gas is given off. Sometimes a solid forms. We have discovered that compounds can react with each other. We are going to mix two more compounds to make paint!

practical activity   Making paint

Be safe: *Lead nitrate is toxic. Do not put your fingers into your mouth. Wash your hands after the experiment*

You need the following apparatus: two small beakers, conical flask, filter paper, filter funnel. You also need chemicals: lead nitrate solution, potassium iodide solution.

1 Put about 25 cm^3 of lead nitrate solution into one beaker.
2 Put about 25 cm^3 of potassium iodide solution into another beaker.
3 Carefully add the potassium iodide solution to the lead nitrate solution
4 Set up the apparatus as shown in Figure 4. Filter the mixture, and then open the filter paper to see the yellow solid. You will also have a colourless liquid in the conical flask.

The yellow solid you have just made is the yellow pigment in some paints which are no longer used to paint toys. Toy manufacturers have had to recall toys from shops because the paint used in the toys contained lead. Children often put toys into their mouths and chew them. The paint you made contains lead, and is toxic.

extension activity   Dangerous paints

Use the internet to find out why lead is so dangerous. Find out what is used to make safe paints.

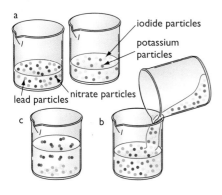

Figure 5 The lead particles (shown in green) join with the iodide particles (shown in yellow) to form lead iodide. The potassium particles (shown in blue) join with the nitrate particles (shown in red) to form potassium nitrate.

Let's try to understand what has happened in the reaction in the practical activity. Look at the diagrams in Figure 5. The lead particles have joined up with the iodide particles. They have formed a new compound called lead iodide. This is the compound in the yellow paint. The other substance left behind in the water is potassium nitrate, which is soluble in water. The lead iodide is insoluble and so it forms a solid.

1 **Describe what happens when copper sulphate solution is mixed with ammonia solution. Do you think a reaction has taken place?**
2 **What sort of observations would you expect to see if a reaction had taken place between two compounds?**
3 **Draw diagrams to explain what happens to the lead particles when a solution of lead nitrate is mixed with potassium iodide solution.**
4 **Why does the lead iodide form a solid?**

→ 5.4 What's in a bottle of mineral water?

→ **In this unit we are learning that:**

■ materials can be classified as elements, compounds and mixtures
■ mixtures do not have a fixed composition, and cannot be represented by a chemical formula
■ the particles in a mixture are not chemically joined together.

Figure 1 What is in this bottle?

You may have a bottle of mineral water in your school bag. Do you ever read the labels to find out what is in the bottle? Is it just water, the chemical compound H_2O, or is there something added to the water? It may be described as fresh spring water, which means it has been collected from a natural source.

Ca	40.5	Cl	8.1
Mg	11.6	SO₄	6.4

Figure 2 The water contains other elements and compounds. The figures show the number of mg/l of each.

activity

Looking at labels on bottles

Examine the labels on the samples of mineral water you have in the classroom. Make a list of all the substances mentioned on the label. Have you found any chemical element names? Are there any names of compounds?

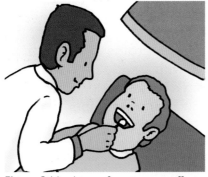

Figure 3 Hard or soft water can affect teeth.

Look at the label shown in Figure 2. There is a list of chemical substances in the water. Calcium ions are often present, and these are good for our healthy teeth and bones. If there is a lot of calcium in the water, chemists describe this as hard water. Some of the water in County Fermanagh near Marble Arch Caves is hard. The water in the Belfast area is described as soft. This is because it does not contain much calcium. Dentists are quite concerned about how soft or hard water affects our teeth.

extension activity

Hard water and your teeth

1 Use the internet to find out more about hard water and its effect on teeth. Next time you're at the dentist, ask about the local water and how it can affect your teeth.
2 Would you like to be a dentist or a dental nurse? Find out more about these jobs.

investigation Boiling mineral water

1 Put about 100 cm³ of mineral water into a beaker.
2 Heat the water until it boils. (See Figure 4.) Continue boiling for about 5 minutes.
3 Allow the water to cool. Describe any changes you notice.

Figure 4 Heating mineral water.

When some types of mineral water are boiled, the calcium forms a compound which is insoluble in the water. This compound is calcium carbonate. You will learn more about this substance in Chapter 8 when you look at rocks. The skin which forms on the water is a thin layer of calcium carbonate. Some of it will also be found lying at the bottom of the beaker.

We are interested in the question: *Are there other sorts of materials apart from elements and compounds?* Mineral water is described as a mixture of substances. You may have eaten dolly mixtures like those in Figure 5.

Figure 5 How would you sort these dolly mixtures?

activity Exploring the differences between elements, mixtures, and compounds.

1 Sort out the dolly mixture sweets in your packet into different groups according to their shape.
2 Now sort out the groups into different colours.
3 Compare your packet of sweets to the other groups in the class. Do you all have the same number of jellies? Is the number of round sweets the same? Have all the groups got the same number of brown sweets?

Mixtures are different from compounds in that they contain a random selection of particles. No two packets of dolly mixtures have exactly the same contents. They may have the same number of grams in mass, but the distribution of sweets is random. However, compounds always have a fixed ratio of atoms.

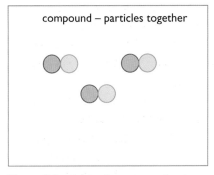

activity Sweet models of molecules

I Take two square sweets and place one round one beside them, as in Figure 6. This could represent a molecule of water: two hydrogen atoms and one oxygen atom.

2 Try making some more compounds using the sweets, for example: carbon dioxide, hydrogen chloride, ammonia.

3 How would you represent molecules of elements, for example oxygen, O_2, and nitrogen, N_2?

Remember that the atoms of an element are all the same. The sweets model is limited in that it cannot show the atoms joined together.

Figure 6

compound – particles together	element – particles all the same	mixture – particles different
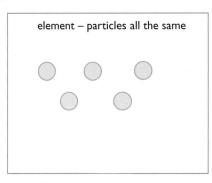		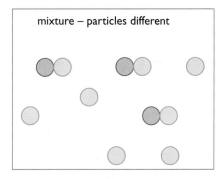

Figure 7 Particles of compounds, elements and mixtures.

Look at the pictures in Figure 7 showing particles of compounds, elements and mixtures. We now know that materials can be made of elements, compounds or mixtures. Figure 8 shows some examples of important mixtures.

Figure 8 Some important mixtures.

I What is a 'mixture'? Give three examples of mixtures.

2 What substance in mineral water is good for teeth and bones?

3 Draw diagrams to show how particles are arranged in elements, mixtures and compounds.

4 Describe an experiment to show that mineral water contains dissolved substances.

5 Sort out the following substances into elements, compounds and mixtures: water, salt, copper, air, crude oil, helium, carbon dioxide, calcium carbonate, soil, oxygen.

→ 5.5 What is a pure substance?

> → **In this unit we are learning that:**
>
> - elements and compounds melt and boil at particular temperatures
> - the melting and boiling points can be used to identify substances
> - mixtures do not melt or boil at fixed temperatures.

Figure 1 'Pure' substances.

What do we mean by the word 'pure' when it is applied to a material? Pure orange juice means that it has come directly from oranges and has nothing else added to it. Other cartons of orange juice may have sugar added or they may be diluted with water. Pure oxygen means that the cylinder contains only oxygen and not the other gases which are in the air. Pure carbon dioxide means that the cylinder contains only carbon dioxide.

In Unit 1.4 we learned that the different gases in the air can be separated using the process of **fractional distillation**. This process depends on the fact that each gas has its own unique boiling point. All elements and compounds have their own melting and boiling points which can be found in a data book (see Figure 2).

Figure 2 Data book.

---

activity Using data to find the boiling and melting points of common substances

Figure 3 Some common substances.

Your teacher will show you a data book with information about melting and boiling points. The internet also gives you information on melting and boiling points.

Working in pairs, make a table to record your findings for the boiling and melting points of some common substances. You should include some metals, some solids you use at home such as salt (listed as sodium chloride), and sugar (sucrose), and also some of the gases in the air such as helium and oxygen.

Changes of state of pure elements and compounds occur at fixed temperatures, and these temperatures are characteristic of the substance. Did you find the melting point or boiling point of air in the data book? Air does not have a fixed melting point or boiling point because it is a mixture.

investigation   Comparing boiling temperatures

In this activity you will compare the boiling temperatures of tap water and salt (sodium chloride) solutions of different strengths.

1 Put 20 grams of salt into a conical flask, and add 100 cm³ of water.
2 Put 10 grams of salt into another conical flask, and add 100 cm³ of water.
3 Put 100 cm³ of water into a third conical flask.
4 Heat all three flasks and record the boiling temperatures.
5 Compare your results with other groups in the class.

Figure 4 Comparing boiling points.

Pure water boils at 100 °C. Salt water boils at a slightly higher temperature. The boiling temperature of the salt water depends on the amount of salt in the water. It does not have a fixed boiling temperature.

This is typical of mixtures, and we can use the boiling point of a liquid to decide if a substance is pure or impure. Ethanol is another liquid. It has a boiling point of 78 °C. When water is added to ethanol it does not have a fixed boiling point and can boil at any temperature between 78 °C and 100 °C, depending on the amount of water added.

Figure 5 Finding the boiling point of a mixture of water and ethanol.

investigation Melting and cooling stearic acid

You need the following apparatus: a clean dry boiling tube, a 400 cm^3 beaker, a thermometer and eye protection. You also need chemicals: stearic acid and water.

Be safe: You must wear eye protection

1 Put the stearic acid into a boiling tube up to a depth of 5 cm, and place a thermometer in the powder.
2 Set the boiling tube into a beaker of hot water at about 75 °C.
3 Heat the water gently and stir the powder until all the stearic acid melts.
4 Remove the boiling tube from the hot water and start to record the temperature every minute. Continue for about 10 minutes.
5 Draw a graph of your results. Put time in minutes on the x-axis, and temperature on the y-axis.
6 Describe what you have found out from the graph. Can you tell what the freezing point of the stearic acid is from the graph?

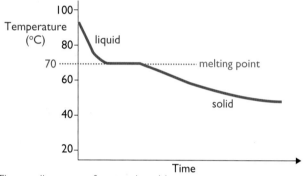

Figure 6 The cooling curve for stearic acid.

Freezing and melting points always happen at the same temperature for pure samples of a particular substance. Pure stearic acid always melts or freezes at 69.6 °C

What do you think would happen to the melting point if the stearic acid was contaminated with another solid? Your teacher may let you try the experiment again to see if you are correct.

extension activity What is stearic acid?

Did you notice that it felt greasy? Use the internet to find out more about it. Find out how to make soap.

1 **What is meant by the term 'pure substance'?**
2 **Describe how you could find out whether or not a sample of water was pure.**
3 **Make a list of five metallic elements and find their melting points.**
4 **Why is it difficult to melt salt in the laboratory? You may need to consult a data book.**

→ 5.6 How can we summarise science information?

→ **In this unit we are learning:**

■ to identify key information on a topic
■ to summarise science information.

In the early chapters of this book you have been learning about a range of topics. You probably find it difficult to remember all you would like to about these themes. One way to help you understand and remember is to write summaries or reports.

Figure 1 Learning in science.

activity Identifying useful information

1 Choose a theme that interests you from Chapters 1 to 5. Make a list of the information and ideas you want to remember about this. Decide which three or four of these you think are most important. You can use activity sheet *X11 Making a summary* to help you.

2 Identify and record at least three sources you can use to find the information you need. One of these should be on paper, like a book or magazine, one a website and, if possible, one should be someone you can discuss the topic with. Remember that websites (and sometimes books and people) aren't always reliable, and it is useful to check the information carefully against other sources. Discuss with the other members of your class how you can decide whether the information presented on a website is reliable.

3 Make rough notes to help you answer your questions. These can be on a spray diagram or bullet points. Use information from as many of your reliable sources as possible.

activity Writing your summary

1 Write, or word process, a first draft of your summary, including:
– An **introduction** (about 5 to 15% of the total word count). This should briefly describe the background, and outline how you intend to develop your theme.
– A **development** (about 80%). This should be written as a series of paragraphs, each answering one of your questions, or describing a single topic.
– A **conclusion** (also about 5 to 15%). This should look back at the introduction, and give the reader the main message of the summary. It should not include new material.
Use pictures and diagrams as much as possible to help explain your ideas.

2 Revise your first draft. You may want to print this out, and then make amendments on paper, or you may prefer to work on screen. Show your draft to others in your group and check that they can understand it. If they can't, revise it again. Produce a final draft with a title, and list your sources of information at the end.

6 How does electricity work?

→ 6.1 How do electrical circuits work?

→ **In this unit, we are learning:**

- to represent objects using symbols
- to make and test predictions about electrical conduction
- to use an analogy to help describe an idea (personal understanding).

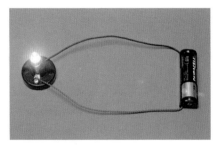

Figure 1 This circuit is shown in a diagram form in Figure 2.

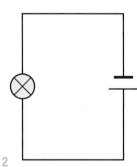

Figure 2

An **electric circuit** is a path along which electricity can flow. Look at the circuit in Figure 1. The bulb lights because the circuit has no gaps. It is a complete circuit. If you want to turn the bulb on and off easily a switch is needed. A switch works by opening and closing a gap in the circuit.

It is difficult to draw the circuit components, but we can describe the circuit using electrical symbols. Table 1 shows symbols for the electrical components you will use.

Table 1 Symbols of electrical components.

Component	Symbol	Component	Symbol
cell	—⊣⊢—	ammeter	—Ⓐ—
battery	—⊣⊢⊣⊢—	voltmeter	—Ⓥ—
connecting wire	——	fixed resistor	—▭—
switch (open)	—⌿∘—	variable resister	—⟋—
switch (closed)	—∘∘—	diode	—◄—

Figure 3 Symbols on roadsides.

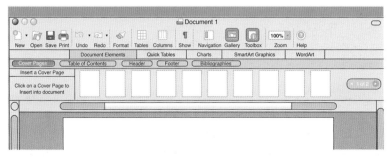

Figure 4 Symbols on a computer program toolbar.

1 **Why is a symbol diagram better than a drawing or a word description to record a circuit?**
2 **Where else in science are symbols used?**
3 **Figures 3 and 4 show some examples of symbols often used in everyday life. Why are symbols useful here?**

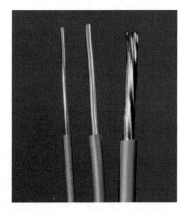

What's the connection?

Copper wires covered in plastic are used to connect up electrical circuits. Copper is a **conductor** as it allows electricity to flow through it. Plastic is an **insulator** as it does not allow electricity to flow through it. Why is it necessary to cover the copper conducting wires with plastic?

Figure 5 Connecting wire cut to show the wires inside.

activity Will it? Won't it?

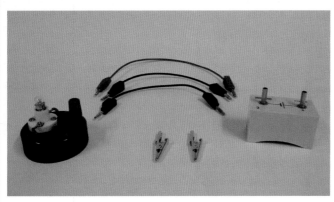

Figure 6 A cell, a bulb, two crocodile clips and connecting wires.

1 Draw a diagram of a circuit which can be used to test a substance to see whether it is a conductor or an insulator using the components in Figure 6.
2 Predict whether the following substances are conductors or insulators: copper, aluminium, glass, paper, rubber, carbon, wool, plastic, air and iron. Predictions should not be just guesses. What have you based your predictions on?
3 Build your circuit and test your predictions.
4 What conclusions can you draw from your results?

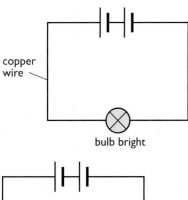

copper wire

bulb bright

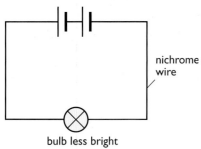

nichrome wire

bulb less bright

Figure 7 Why is the brightness of the bulb different?

Why copper? Would any metal do?

What is the difference between the two circuits in Figure 7? Why is the bulb in the circuit with the copper wire brighter? Would any metal work to connect circuits?

It is more difficult for a current to go through nichrome than through copper. Nichrome resists the current more than copper. Nichrome has a bigger **resistance** than copper.

Every material has an electrical resistance. The greater the material's resistance the smaller the current that flows through it. Conductors have low resistance. Insulators have high resistance. Resistance is measured in ohms, named after the German scientist Georg Ohm, who carried out many experiments investigating resistance in the 1820s.

A piece of wire which offers some resistance to a current is called a **resistor**. Resistors are components which are designed to reduce current in a circuit. A dimmer switch is an example of a **variable resistor**, which is a component whose resistance can be changed by turning a knob.

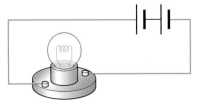

Figure 8 A circuit to light a bulb.

Energy

When a current flows through a wire, electrical energy is changed to heat energy. When a current is pushed through a high resistance, large amounts of heat energy are produced. This is what happens in heating elements, like in electric fires.

4 **The light bulb in Figure 8 contains some metal with a high resistance, some metal with a low resistance, and an insulator. Which parts are made of each of these materials?**

practical activity Make a dimmer switch

Connect the second crocodile clip in Figure 9 with two different lengths of eureka wire between the clips. Is there any change in brightness? This shows that when a short length of eureka wire is used, the lamp glows brightly. However, when a much longer piece is used, it is harder for the current to flow and the light becomes dimmer.

Figure 9 How can this circuit be used to produce a variable brightness?

Figure 10 Power cables. There are porcelain or glass connectors from the pylons to the cables.

5 **There are many variable resistors in appliances around your home. Can you name some?**
6 **Explain why electricity cables are made of thick aluminium wire, connected to steel pylons by porcelain or glass connectors.**
7 **Water is a poor conductor, but it can conduct a large enough current from mains electricity to kill you. Wet skin conducts better than dry skin. Use these facts to explain how a lie detector works, and why bathrooms have pull cord light switches.**

Figure 11 Lie detector test.

Figure 12 Bathroom light switch.

activity Traffic analogy

An **analogy** is a useful tool to describe a scientific idea, because it can help us understand things better. Sometimes the flow of electricity is compared to the flow of traffic. Match these comparisons with the most suitable aspect of electric current.

Figure 13

Traffic conditions
motorway with busy quick moving traffic
bumpy quiet country lane
landslide road closed impassable
level crossing barrier down
level crossing barrier up

Electrical circuits
insulator
switch closed
good conductor large current
switch open
poor conductor small current

Can you think of a different analogy to help describe electric current?

practical activity One way traffic

Figure 14 A turnstile.

A diode is an electrical component which has a low resistance to current flowing one way and an extremely high resistance to current flowing the other way. Use a diode in a simple circuit to investigate which way round the diode has high resistance.
The diode is often compared to a football turnstile. Why?

8 **What word describes each of the following?**
   - **The flow of electrons.**
   - **More than one electrical cell.**
   - **Material which will not allow electricity to flow.**
   - **Material which will allow electricity to flow.**
   - **A component which only allows current to flow in one direction.**

6.2 What happens in an electrical circuit?

In this unit, we are learning:

- to measure electric current with an ammeter
- that cells are a source of electrical energy
- to identify variables in an investigation.

An electric current is the flow of negatively charged particles called electrons. If you want to measure the size of the current you need to put a **meter** into the circuit. Current is measured in **amperes** (A), or amps for short, after the French physicist André Ampère. The meter that measures current flowing through it is called an **ammeter**. You can find the symbol for an ammeter in Table 1 of Unit 6.1.

You learned in Unit 1.5 that the atoms in all materials contain electrons. One ampere is equivalent to 1.6 million million million electrons passing a point in a circuit each second.

activity Investigating ammeter readings

1 Look carefully at the circuit in Figure 1. Describe how the ammeter is connected into the circuit.
2 Draw the symbol diagram for this circuit.
3 Set up the circuit and investigate the effect of adding more bulbs and more cells. Try different numbers of each.
4 Record your observations of the ammeter reading, and the brightness of the bulb.
5 What happens when you change over the connections to the ammeter?
6 What is the relationship between the brightness of the bulb and the ammeter reading?

Note that putting an ammeter in the circuit does not affect the current. It behaves just like a connecting wire.

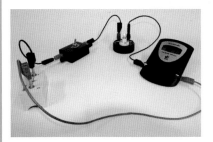

Figure 1 A circuit with a cell, a switch, a bulb and an ammeter.

A **battery** is actually the name for a group of single **cells** connected together in a circuit (see Figure 2).

What does the cell do?

The **cell's** job is to push the electric current around the circuit, by giving the electrons extra energy. The push which the cell gives the electrons is called the **voltage**. It is measured in volts (V) on a **voltmeter**. The first battery of cells was made by the Italian scientist Alessandro Volta in the 1790s.

Different cells can provide different voltages. The bigger the voltage the bigger the current that flows in the circuit. Most commonly used cells provide only 1.5V but you can get a bigger voltage by using several cells together – forming a battery.

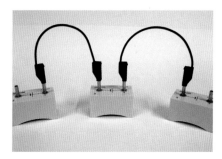

Figure 2 Three connected cells.

Figure 3 A variety of cells and batteries.

Figure 4 Different sized cells can have the same voltage.

1 **What pumps the blood around your body?**

2 **How does the water in your central heating travel around the pipes?**

3 **What do the cells in Figure 4 have in common? How do they differ? Explain what will happen if these cells are each connected to identical bulbs. Will the light in the bulbs last for the same amount of time? Will the brightness of the bulbs differ?**

A cell contains chemicals which act to make one side of the cell positively charged and one side negatively charged. This gives the energy difference needed for the electrons to flow. The chemical energy of the cell is changed to electrical energy. This chemical energy is used up by pushing electrons in the current round the circuit.

When something flows, an energy difference is required. When water flows, there is a difference in height such as a mountain, or a difference in pressure as in a tap. If you want to 'flow' on your skateboard, you need a difference in height. There is a difference in the gravitational potential energy at the top of a slope or hill compared to the bottom. Something has more potential energy at the top of the hill than at the bottom.

If current is to flow, a difference in voltage is required: this is called electrical **potential difference**. The voltage or potential difference provided by the battery is the 'pump' that pushes the electrons around the circuit.

investigation Make a fruit cell

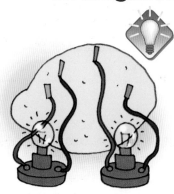

1 The acid inside fruit can be used as the chemicals to make an electric cell. How would you investigate which fruits make the greatest voltage and which metals are most effective for the electrodes? What other variables could be investigated?

2 For each variable you are investigating, identify the dependent, independent and controlled variables. Why is it important to do this?

Figure 5 A lemon with electrodes of different colours representing different metals lighting up a bulb.

6.3 Are all circuits simple?

➡ **In this unit, we are learning:**

- to construct parallel circuits
- to identify patterns in measurements
- to collaborate with others to solve problems.

investigation Series and parallel

What is the difference between the two circuits in Figure 1? Both have a cell and two bulbs. See for yourself!

1 Set up circuits A and B and observe the brightness of the bulbs.
2 Record what happens when one of the bulbs is unscrewed in each circuit.
3 What happens when more bulbs are added?

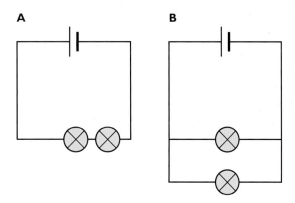

A B

Figure 1

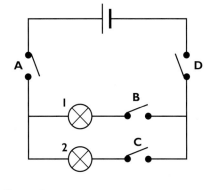

Figure 2

In circuit A the bulbs are joined in **series**. The more bulbs which are added in circuits like this, the dimmer they become. If one is removed all the others stop working.

In circuit B the bulbs are joined in **parallel**. The bulbs stay bright and either bulb can be unscrewed without affecting the other. Each bulb has the full driving force of the cell across it. It is as if each one were connected separately to the cell, but the cell's energy will be used up twice as quickly.

1 **What happens to the brightness if you keep adding more bulbs in parallel?**
2 **Why are the lights in your house wired in parallel?**
3 **Which switches control the current through bulb 1 in Figure 2?**

activity Parallel circuits

What happens to the current in a parallel circuit?
Set up circuit B (Figure 1) and use an ammeter to measure the current at different places in the circuit. Use your observations to describe what happens to the current in the circuit.

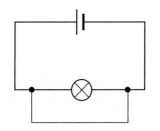

Figure 3

Is there a problem?

The bulb in Figure 3 will not light. Electricity always takes the path of lowest resistance. The bulb filament is high resistance, and the wire is low resistance. The current takes the easier path around the bulb. The bulb does not light up as very little current goes through it – just like most drivers prefer to take a by-pass road around a busy town, as there would be less traffic to slow them down.

activity Series and parallel circuits

In a group, look at the circuits in Figure 5. Discuss each one and say whether each bulb will glow with normal brightness (Figure 4), brighter, dimmer or not at all.

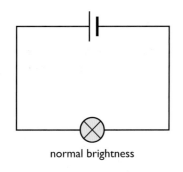

normal brightness

Figure 4

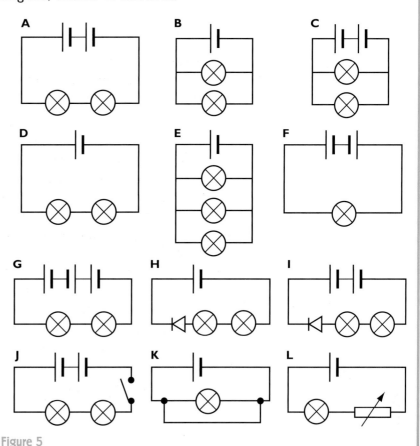

Figure 5

→ 6.4 What is the relationship between voltage and current?

→ **In this unit, we are learning:**

- to investigate the relationship between current and voltage
- how different electrical components behave
- how to represent relationships on graphs.

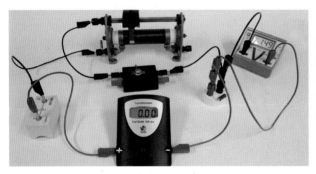

The current through an electrical component depends on the voltage you apply across it. To measure the voltage across a component, a **voltmeter** must be connected in **parallel** with the component. To measure the current through a component an ammeter must be connected in **series** with the component.

Figure 1 A circuit with a variable resistor, cell, switch, resistor, voltmeter and ammeter.

investigation Variation of current with voltage

You can use the circuit in Figure 1 to investigate how the current through a component changes with the voltage across it. What is the variable resistor for?

1 Draw the diagram for this circuit.
2 Set up the circuit, and obtain results to show how the voltage across the resistor varies with the current through it.
3 Different components give different results. Replace the resistor by a filament bulb. Draw the circuit diagram to investigate the variation of current through the bulb with voltage.
4 Draw a graph to show how voltage varies with current through the bulb.
5 For the resistor, describe as carefully as you can how the current through the resistor changes as the voltage is increased. Use some of the statements in Figure 3 to help you.
6 Investigate the graph for the filament bulb. Describe your graph for a filament bulb and explain how it differs from that of a resistor.

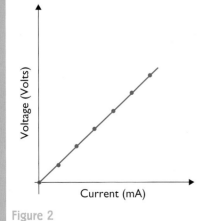

Figure 2

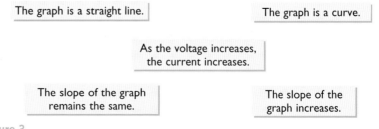

The graph is a straight line.

The graph is a curve.

As the voltage increases, the current increases.

The slope of the graph remains the same.

The slope of the graph increases.

Figure 3

Georg Ohm investigated this relationship, and formed a law known as **Ohm's Law,** which says that, *for a conductor at constant temperature, the current through the conductor is proportional to the voltage across it.* This means that, if the graph is a straight line through the origin, it agrees with this law. If, for example, the voltage is doubled the current also doubles.

Look at the graph in Figure 2, and the graph you got from the experiment with the bulb. Which agrees with Ohm's Law?

Ohm also found during his investigations that the slope of a graph of voltage against current showed the resistance of the component. If the slope is constant, the resistance is constant. If the slope is curved, the resistance changes. The greater the slope, the greater the resistance.

1 **What happens to the resistance of the resistor, and to the resistance of the bulb?**
2 **What physical property, mentioned in Ohm's Law, changes when the current through a bulb is increased?**

→ 6.5 Who are the bright sparks?

→ In this unit, we are learning:

- how understanding about electricity has developed over time (cultural awareness)
- about a career using science related skills (employability).

activity ## Bright sparks in history

Many scientists have contributed to our understanding of electricity. One scientist (Luigi Galvani) is famous for passing electric current through frogs' legs! Some famous physicists who worked with electricity have already been mentioned in this chapter, for example: Ohm, Ampère and Volta. Other famous electrical scientists include Michael Faraday, Benjamin Franklin, Thomas Edison and Charles Coulomb.

1 Make a time line with the date and contribution of these and other scientists to the history of electricity.
2 Discuss with your group which scientist made the greatest contribution to this area of science.

Figure 1 Who is this, and what is he doing? Note that this is very dangerous and you must *not* try it yourself!

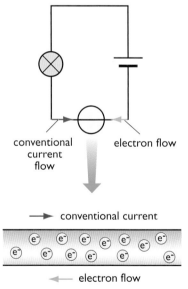

conventional current flow electron flow

conventional current

electron flow

Figure 2 Conventional current flow.

Science was wrong!

We now know that electric current is the flow of electrons. Although electrons actually travel from the negative terminal of a cell to the positive terminal, circuit diagrams usually show current going the other way. This direction was agreed by convention in the nineteenth century, before electrons were discovered.

This apparent current flow is called conventional current. We should now disregard conventional flow as we know it is incorrect, but much of the science of electricity was developed when this type of current flow was believed to be correct – so it is still used. Negative electrons going in one direction have exactly the same effect as conventional current going in the opposite direction.

Can you think of any other areas of science where new knowledge has shown science to be incorrect?

That's the job!

At the flick of a switch, a light comes on. At the touch of a button, electricity rushes almost instantaneously to the television. It is hard to imagine life without this basic convenience. Whom can we thank for electricity safely zapping its way around our homes, schools, hospitals, shops and cinemas? Electricians!

I am an electrician who works in construction. I read blueprints to wire, install and test electrical systems. It's a very interesting job.

I am an electrician working in maintenance. I test and fix malfunctioning electrical systems. It's a worthwhile job.

I am an apprentice electrician and split my time between college and work. I will qualify with certificates in technical skills and safety. I will earn as much as someone with a university degree. It's a very satisfying job.

I enjoy working with my hands. I feel constantly challenged with problem solving situations. I work in a great variety of locations. Safety is my top priority as there is always the risk of electric shock. Also, people's safety is in our hands. You must have a careful eye for detail.

Figure 3 Views of electricians.

1 **What skills do you develop as an electrician?**
2 **Why is safety such an important aspect of this job?**
3 **How would you describe an electrician's job?**

→ 6.6 How can we find out more about science using the media?

→ **In this unit we are learning:**

■ to use newspapers and magazines to find out how science works (media awareness)
■ to clarify our ideas about a science issue (safety of power lines)
■ to assess the reliability of newspaper/magazine reports on science issues (media awareness)
■ how science investigations become public (media awareness).

Many people are afraid of electricity. Our ancestors knew that lightning killed people, and we know that people can die through the careless use of electrical equipment. However, some people also worry about the unseen radiation from electrical equipment and installations such as microwave ovens and mobile phones, power lines and transformers.

Figure 1 Some people worry about living close to power lines.

activity Finding out about power lines

People are concerned about living near high voltage overhead power lines. They are unsure whether this is safe or not. Use the BBC website, and the sites of some newspapers and magazines, local and national, and key 'power lines' into their search engine. You might look at some letters to the editor, but remember that these are usually written from a particular viewpoint, and may be biased. Note down three points from your newspaper search (other than from letters). Compare your results with the rest of your group.

You want to find out if living near power lines is dangerous. However, you also want to know if you can rely on the information provided. To do this, it's useful to find out how the information was obtained. You need to know something about the nature of scientific enquiry.

You are already familiar with the importance of fair testing. You also know that you need to record and average a number of readings to get a more accurate result, and to rule out mistakes. Scientists also try to ensure that their reports are accurate by accepting 'peer review'. That is, for other scientists to read and comment on their draft reports before their paper is published in a scientific journal. They also emphasise that their results are not final: they may be improved by later scientists using more effective methods and techniques.

Figure 2 Peer review.

activity Assessing reports

Choose two of the reports you have found in your search. You will want to know how reliable these are. Are they based on results from a fair experiment, which can be repeated by other scientists?

Some questions you might ask about the reports are listed below. Although you are unlikely to get answers to all of them, you may get enough information to decide whether the report is reliable or not. You may find activity sheet *X15 Assessing reports* useful. Do the activity on your own first, then compare your answers with a partner, and come to an agreed response.

First, list the two or three key conclusions of the investigation. Then assess the reliability of the report by answering the following questions.

1 How was the research carried out? Are all the steps clearly stated? Was the sample size large enough to give significant results?

2 What is the background to the report? Who did the research? Why? Who paid for it? How were the researchers connected to the source of their finance?

3 How did the researchers come to a conclusion? What data were collected? How? What conclusions were drawn? Were these justified by the original data? How much confidence do the researchers place on their conclusions? Where did the researchers report their conclusions?

4 What did other scientists think about the research and its conclusions? Do they support it? What do non-scientists (government or general public) think? Have there been other investigations in the same area? If so, do they agree?

5 What newspaper/magazine does the report appear in? Who wrote the article: scientist or newspaper reporter? Is there a newspaper campaign related to the story? Can I get information on this story from other sources? If so, do they agree?

6 How important is the report to me, to others in the local community, to people in Northern Ireland?

Respiration: lungs and blood

→ ## 7.1 Burning up?

> → **In this unit we are learning:**
>
> ■ to improve mathematical skills in calculating personal energy needs
> ■ understand the need to balance energy intake with energy use in exercise (personal health)
> ■ to make inferences about daily energy needs and energy expenditure
> ■ to research and debate a scientific topic (mutual understanding).

Figure 1 A body that has been burned.

Spontaneous human combustion: myth or reality?

Spontaneous Human Combustion (SHC) is a scientific hypothesis. It suggests that the human body can catch fire automatically, without being set alight by a flame. There is, however, much disagreement about SHC. Many ideas have been put forward to explain SHC. Some ideas are suggested by scientists, but most are not believed. In the debate at the end of this unit, you can help to find an answer to this question.

Fires release more heat energy if there is more fuel present. When a fuel is burned in **oxygen**, **carbon dioxide** and water are formed, and energy is released. This reaction is **combustion** that you learned about in Year 8. In the cells of the human body, energy is released by a similar chemical reaction called **respiration**. However, the reaction of respiration is more controlled than combustion, to prevent your cells being damaged. The word equations for these reactions are:

combustion:
fuel + oxygen → carbon dioxide + water (+ light and heat energy)

respiration:
glucose + oxygen → carbon dioxide + water (+ energy)

Figure 2 When you run, you need more energy.

Respiration occurs to provide the energy that your body uses all the time. Energy is required to keep your heart beating, and your brain needs energy for thinking. The amount of energy that you use just to keep you alive is your baseline energy need or **Basal Metabolic Rate (BMR)**, and it is different for different people.

When you perform an activity such as running or playing tennis you need even more energy. This is why after exercise you often feel tired because your body has used extra energy. Active people use up lots more energy than people who take little exercise. Activity has other health benefits too, such as making your heart and your muscles stronger.

activity How much energy do you need?

This activity will show you how much energy is used daily. You will calculate and compare the BMR values for a teenage boy and a teenage girl by following the steps in Table 1. You can also calculate your own BMR.

There is a set of instructions, put forward by scientists Arthur Harris and Francis Benedict, that you should follow to calculate your total daily energy needs. These instructions are shown in Table 2.

Your teacher may give you an activity sheet to help you, and you should use a calculator. Note that the result you get in Step 6 is in kilocalories; many dieticians and sports scientists still use this unit. To find your BMR in kilojoules, multiply this figure by 4.2.

	For boys	For girls
1	Multiply the mass in kilograms by 13.8. This is measurement A.	Multiply the mass in kilograms by 9.6. This is measurement A.
2	Multiply the height in centimetres by 5. This is measurement B.	Multiply the height in centimetres by 1.9. This is measurement B.
3	Add together the values of A and B. This is measurement C.	Add together the values of A and B. This is measurement C.
4	Add 66.5 to value C. This is measurement D.	Add 665 to value C. This is measurement D.
5	Multiply age by 6.8. This is measurement E.	Multiply age by 4.7. This is measurement E.
6	Work out (value for D) – (value for E). This is the BMR measurement in kilocalories.	Work out (value for D) – (value for E). This is the BMR measurement in kilocalories.
7	Multiply this Figure by 4.2. This is the BMR measurement in kilojoules.	Multiply this Figure by 4.2. This is the BMR measurement in kilojoules.

Table 1 Steps in calculating BMR for boys and girls.

Harris Benedict Formula

To determine your total daily energy needs, multiply your BMR by the activity factor that you think applies to you.

1. If you are sedentary (little or no exercise) daily energy need = BMR × 1.2

2. If you are lightly active (light exercise/sports 1-3 days/week) = BMR × 1.375

3. If you are moderately active (moderate exercise/sports 3-5 days/week) = BMR × 1.55

4. If you are very active (hard exercise/sports 6-7 days a week) = BMR × 1.725

5. If you are extra active (very hard exercise/sports and physical job or 2x training) = BMR × 1.9

Table 2 The Harris Benedict Formula.

Figure 3 a This lady is washing clothes by hand. b It is easier to wash clothes in a machine.

Exercise has many health benefits. Doctors recommend that we exercise daily, particularly in activities that cause us to take deep breaths. This type of exercise is called **aerobic exercise**. Compared with people in the 1950s, people in today's society take much less exercise. This might be because of the development of appliances such as the washing machine that mean people are less physically active today than in the 1950s. You could compile a class list of activities that have been made easier because of new appliances.

---

extension activity Exercise for health

Search the internet and other sources to find out more information about the benefits of different types of exercise on health. Use this information to design a leaflet for upper primary pupils to encourage them to become more active. The leaflet should help them to understand the ways in which exercise can improve their health.

Activity	Amount of energy used (kJ/minute)
Walking slowly	13
Light gardening	15
Walking uphill	36
Swimming	30
Cycling	40
Digging	33
Jogging	26
Walking quickly	21
Playing football	40

Table 3 Amount of energy used for various activities.

---

activity Spontaneous Human Combustion (SHC): myth or reality?

You are asked to debate the issue of SHC. You can download activity sheet *X7 Debating* to help manage your ideas. Your teacher will organise the class members into groups. Each group will be given a particular view: either in support of, or opposed to, the idea that SHC occurs naturally. It will be your task to find out more about the topic and to present evidence that supports your views. You could search the internet, books and encyclopaedias. You could even imagine that someone in the place where you live is claiming that a local death is an example of SHC.

---

1 **Suggest why people sometimes ignore claims made by scientists.**
2 **Explain the meaning of the term 'Basal Metabolic Rate' (BMR).**
3 **Give three reasons for differences in people's BMRs.**
4 **Jack eats a lot of take-away meals. He is obese and is often out of breath. What advice would you suggest to help him to improve his health?**

→ 7.2 The breath of life

→ **In this unit we are learning:**

- to investigate respiration, and the need to breathe oxygen
- to compare and contrast inhaled and exhaled air.

Look back at the word equations for combustion and **respiration** in the previous unit. You should notice that both need oxygen gas to release energy from a fuel. Humans take the oxygen that they need into their bodies by breathing.

investigation | Oxygen for burning

Look back at Unit 1.4.

Be safe: You must wear eye protection

This activity demonstrates that fuels burn more vigorously in the presence of oxygen. This is similar to the tests you did in Unit 1.4. Your teacher will give you four test tubes. Two of the tubes are filled with air, and two are filled with oxygen. You should complete this activity with a partner. One of you will need to operate a timer.

1 Take a wooden splint and light it using the flame of a Bunsen burner.
Quickly blow out the flame and plunge the glowing splint into a test-tube filled with air. Start the timer immediately as the splint enters the tube. Stop the timer when the flame is extinguished, and record the time.

2 Repeat Step 1, but this time replace the tube of air with a test tube filled with oxygen gas.

3 Light a small tealight candle. Place a test tube filled with air over the flame and start the timer. Stop the timer as soon as the flame is extinguished and record the time.

4 Repeat Step 3, but replace the tube of air with a tube filled with oxygen.

5 Compare the results from Steps 1 and 2. Write a sentence to describe them.

6 Compare the results from Steps 3 and 4. Write a sentence to describe them.

7 What does this experiment suggest about the effect that oxygen gas has on combustion?

The air that you breathe in is called **inhaled air**. Each time you inhale, normal air is only 21% oxygen, the gas used for respiration. The other 79% of air is made from gases such as nitrogen and carbon dioxide. Seconds later when you breathe out, this is **exhaled air.** Table 1 shows the percentages of the gases present in inhaled and exhaled air.

Feature	Inhaled air	Exhaled air
Oxygen content	21%	16%
Carbon dioxide content	0.04%	4%
Other gas content	1%	2%
Nitrogen content	78%	78%
Temperature (°C)	21°C	37°C
Water vapour	changeable	saturated

Table 1 Features of inhaled and exhaled air.

practical activity   Comparing inhaled with exhaled air

1 To investigate whether exhaled air contains carbon dioxide gas you can use limewater. If carbon dioxide is added to limewater it changes. Breathe out through a straw into a tube filled with limewater. Describe any differences that you observe in the limewater after you have breathed air into it.

2 Explain the results you obtained.

3 On your own, download activity sheet *X6 Thinking skills: Compare and contrast* to help you examine the differences between inhaled and exhaled air from the information in Table 1.

4 Enter the results into a spreadsheet to create pie charts for inhaled air and exhaled air. Print copies of the charts and stick them into your workbook.

practical activity   Respiration in cells

In this activity you will examine respiration using yeast. This is a type of fungus which is a living organism.

1 Use a measuring cylinder to put 400 ml of water into a 500 ml conical flask.

2 Place the flask into a water bath and heat it until the water reaches a temperature of between 40°C and 45°C.

3 While the water is heating, stretch out a large balloon by inflating and deflating 10 times.

4 Add 15 g of sugar and one packet of active dry yeast to the water in your flask and stir until the sugar dissolves.

5 Using a funnel, transfer the mixture into a plastic bottle.

6 Place the balloon over the neck of the bottle and secure the top with strong tape.

7 Place the bottle in the water bath (see Figure 1) or leave on the bench, and continue to observe the contents of the bottle and the balloon throughout the lesson. Describe and explain what you observe.

8 Look back at the word equation for respiration. Suggest why sugar was used in this activity.

9 Can you suggest a control for this activity?

10 Would you expect this activity to work if you had used boiled yeast? Explain your answer.

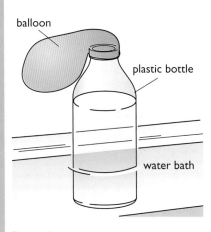

balloon

plastic bottle

water bath

Figure 1

extension activity

Effects of the environment on respiration

Try to suggest ways that you could change the method above to investigate some other features of respiring yeast, for example, the effect of temperature. Remember you must change only one variable at a time, and plan a fair test.

investigation

Breathing

Figure 2

Oxygen and carbon dioxide gas take part in respiration and these enter and leave your lungs when you breathe. Figure 2 shows Jean and her friends discussing what happens during breathing.

1 Discuss each statement with a partner. Do you agree with any of the children? Say whom you agree with, and give reasons why you agree.

2 Do you think air has mass? If you follow the instructions below you will find out the answer to this question.

3 Take a balloon and, before you breathe air into it, place it into a large beaker. Place the beaker on a balance and record the mass.

4 Now fill the balloon with air, either by blowing air into it or by using a hand-pump. Balance the balloon on the top of the beaker to re-weigh.

5 Subtract the mass you recorded in Step 3 from the mass you recorded in Step 4.

6 What did you find out? Does air have mass? Does your finding mean that you need to change your answer to the question in Step 2? If so, explain why you want to change your answer.

1 Name the gases that humans
  a need for respiration
  b produce by respiration.
2 State two differences between inhaled and exhaled air. Explain your answers.

→ 7.3 The respiratory system

> **→ In this unit we are learning:**
>
> - about the structure and functions of the respiratory system
> - to measure and record lung volume
> - to find out about asthma (personal health)
> - to investigate the effects of changes in air pressure
> - to investigate effects of exercise on breathing and heart rate (personal health).

Animals that live on land take air into their **lungs** by breathing. Your lungs are like a pair of balloons that inflate when air enters them and deflate when the air is forced out again. Your teacher may allow you to examine a real pair of animal lungs.

practical activity Changes in lung size with breathing

In this activity you will understand the effect of breathing on the size of your lungs.

Figure 1

1   Place your hands on your ribs and breathe in. Record the direction that your ribs move. Choose from: up and out or down and in.
2   Your lungs move in the same direction as your ribs. They inflate when you breathe in. To examine how the volume of your lungs changes, imagine that your lungs are a pair of balloons. Use a felt tip pen to mark a series of dots on the surface of a balloon then blow air into the balloon. Describe the effect of filling the balloon with air on the spaces between the dots. What does this suggest about how the volume of your lungs changes when you breathe in?
3   Now breathe out. Predict what happens to the volume of your lungs as you do so.
4   Release the air that is trapped inside the balloon. Suggest how the change that you observe in the balloon compares with what happens in your lungs when you breathe out.

The air you breathe travels through a network of vessels before reaching your lungs, where it enters the bloodstream. With your finger, trace on Figure 2 the route that air takes as it flows from your mouth or nose, through the **trachea**, **bronchi** (singular bronchus) **bronchioles** and into the **alveoli** (singular alveolus). You can also observe these structures on the internet: enter 'lungs' into a search engine.

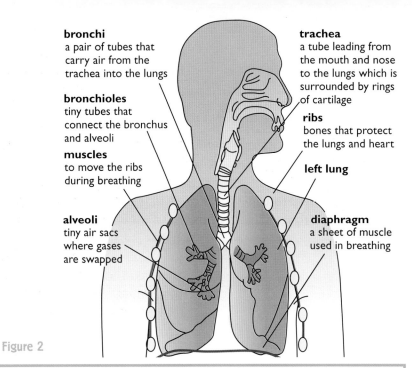

bronchi
a pair of tubes that carry air from the trachea into the lungs

bronchioles
tiny tubes that connect the bronchus and alveoli

muscles
to move the ribs during breathing

alveoli
tiny air sacs where gases are swapped

trachea
a tube leading from the mouth and nose to the lungs which is surrounded by rings of cartilage

ribs
bones that protect the lungs and heart

left lung

diaphragm
a sheet of muscle used in breathing

Figure 2

---

 activity   Finding out about the respiratory system

1. oihbncr	5. eilvaol
2. sloihcbnreo	6. rachtae
3. usgln	7. ghprmiada
4. sirb	

Figure 3

The names of some of the structures in the respiratory system are shown in Figure 3. Unfortunately they have become jumbled. Use the information in Figure 2 to unscramble the name of each structure correctly. Write the answers in your workbook and record alongside each structure the function it performs in the body.

---

practical activity   The pressure of breathing

Be safe: You must wear eye protection. Take care lifting the hot can.

Figure 4

Your teacher will give you a set of large tongs to use. You should also wear eye protection and take care because the steam is very hot and could burn you.

Your lungs are surrounded by the rib cage. This structure is flexible, yet strong. This activity shows what would happen if your rib cage were not able to deal with changes in pressure.

1 You will need an empty drinks can for this activity. Fill the base of the can with approximately 15 ml of water.

2 Place the can on top of a piece of gauze on a tripod stand. Heat the can with a Bunsen burner until the water inside begins to boil. You will see steam and water vapour escaping from the can.

3 Boil the water for a minute then place the large tongs that your teacher will give you around the middle of the can.

4 Keeping the tongs held tightly closed, hold the can over a trough filled with cold water. Turn the can upside down so that some water escapes then immediately plunge the top of the can beneath the surface of the water. You should observe a dramatic effect.

5 Try to explain what happened to the can when it was placed in the trough of water. Hint: think about the how the energy and spacing of the air particles changes when they are heated, compared with when they are rapidly cooled.

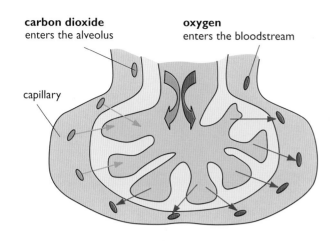

carbon dioxide enters the alveolus

oxygen enters the bloodstream

capillary

Figure 5 Gas exchange in the lungs.

The gases, oxygen and carbon dioxide, enter and leave the cells of the body and travel in the blood stream to the alveoli. There are millions of alveoli and each alveolus is covered by a tiny blood vessel called a **capillary**. Oxygen travels across the wall of the alveoli into the bloodstream while carbon dioxide travels in the opposite direction. This swapping of gases is called **gas exchange** and is shown in Figure 5.

To enable the maximum amount of air to enter and leave the lungs their size is extremely important. This is measured as **lung volume.** Values for lung volume are sometimes taken as a measure of lung function. Reduced lung volume, for example is a feature of the common condition of **asthma**, which affects many people.

Be safe: Pupils who suffer from asthma should not do this activity

practical activity Measuring lung volume

Figure 6 This girl is breathing into a peak flow meter to measure her lung function.

1 You can measure your lung volume using a lung volume bag or a large plastic bottle. Your teacher will tell you how this is done. If you can, collect the results for lung volume for the members of your class.
2 Measure the height of each person. Enter both results onto a spreadsheet and plot a scatter graph. This will allow you to investigate whether there is a link between height and lung volume. You might also search the internet and other sources of information to identify other factors that affect lung volume.

activity Asthma

Search the internet and other sources to find out more information about asthma. What causes it? How can it be treated? Is it a chronic condition? Who is likely to suffer from the condition? Make a PowerPoint presentation to inform the members of your class about asthma.

extension activity How does smoking affect the lungs?

Find out more about the effects of tobacco on the respiratory system. Prepare a leaflet for young children to inform them about the main ingredients of tobacco and how they cause damage to the body.

1 **List the structures of the respiratory system through which air travels through en route from the surroundings to the body cells.**
2 **Explain the term 'gas exchange'.**

→ 7.4 In constant flow

→ **In this unit we are learning:**

- about the structure of the heart
- about the different parts of blood
- about the work of the Northern Ireland Blood Transfusion Service (citizenship)
- to investigate blood related jobs and careers (employability).

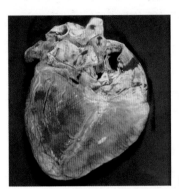

Figure 1 A human heart.

Your **heart** is one of the most vital organs in your body. In fact your heart is a muscle, but it is different to the other muscles in your body. It is made of a special type of muscle, called **cardiac muscle**.

practical activity Tired muscles

Figure 2

1 Hold your arm horizontally at shoulder height in front of your body.
2 Bend your arm at your elbow up and down for at least 30 seconds.
3 Did you find that your arm became tired? What do you think would happen if your heart was made of the same type of muscle that is present in your arm?

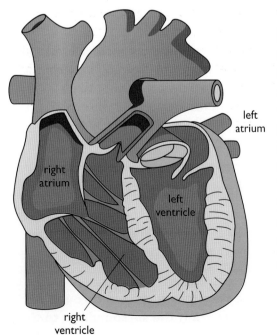

Figure 3 The heart.

Your heart is the size of a closed fist. It is divided in half to create the right-hand side and left-hand side. Each side has two chambers or spaces, the upper chambers are called the **atria** (singular: atrium) and the lower chambers are called the **ventricles**. The pumping action of the heart means that blood continues to travel through the heart. There are many internet sites where you can take a virtual tour through the heart. Key 'heart' into a search engine. If your teacher shows you a heart that has been removed from an animal, try placing your index finger into the different parts of the heart. <u>Ensure you wash your hands thoroughly afterwards.</u>

activity

Blood flow through the heart, and around the body

This activity should help you to follow the pathway that blood takes as it travels through your heart. Members of the class are divided into groups of six pupils each. A diagram of the heart and body organs, including lungs, liver, intestine and kidneys, is placed on the classroom floor, or drawn on the playground. The object of the game is to deliver oxygen to, and remove carbon dioxide gas from, the organs of the body as fast as possible. Note: you must <u>not</u> run. If you do run or make a mistake you must begin the activity again, but the timer will continue to record the time taken.

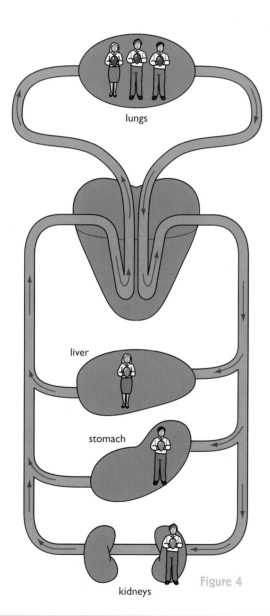

lungs

liver

stomach

kidneys

Figure 4

1 Three members of your group will be given red balloons to represent blood that has oxygen. Three blue balloons will be given to the other members of the group to represent blood that is full of carbon dioxide.

2 The three pupils from the first group each with a red balloon must stand on the lungs. The other three pupils in the group each collect a blue balloon and stand on one of these organs: liver, stomach and kidneys.

3 When the command 'Go' is given, a timer is started. One person from the lungs should walk as quickly as possible through the correct parts of the heart to one of the organs. They must release the air from their balloon, using whatever method they wish.

4 When the air is fully released the team member with a blue balloon standing on that organ starts walking, following the correct path, and when they reach the lungs, they should release the air in their balloon.

5 Repeat Steps 3 and 4 until all six balloons of air have been delivered, the timer is stopped and the time recorded. The second team then takes its turn, and so on. The winning team has the fastest time.

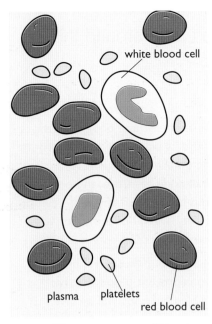

Figure 5 The components of blood.

What is blood?

You know that blood transports oxygen needed for respiration and carbon dioxide produced in respiration. You may be wondering what else blood contains. Blood is a tissue that carries materials such as glucose to the body cells. At the same time, wastes and carbon dioxide are carried away from the body cells. This means that blood must travel in a continuous stream. It contains red and white blood cells and liquid **plasma**.

Last year you studied the two main types of blood cell: red blood cells (which contain a red pigment called haemoglobin that carries oxygen) and white blood cells, which fight germs to prevent disease. Tiny pieces of cells called **platelets** are also present. These help the blood to clot and heal wounds. The liquid part of blood is called plasma and is pale yellow in colour. As well as blood cells, it contains glucose, chemicals and many other proteins.

activity Blood components

Create a spray diagram to present the details about blood. Include details about the structure of each of the four components as well as their functions. You may decide to include drawings of the four parts.

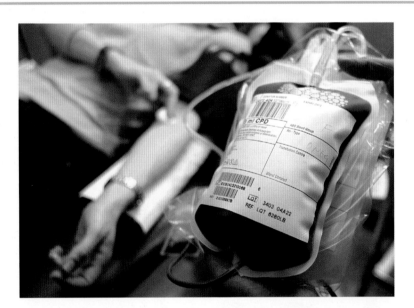

Figure 6 This sample of blood has just been donated.

Sometimes people require a **blood transfusion**. This means that they receive a supply of blood from another person. Members of the public, called **blood donors**, give blood freely. The Northern Ireland Blood Transfusion Service (NIBTS) collects these samples. The National Blood Service in England and North Wales conducts research to improve the safety of blood. **Biomedical scientists** examine the samples to ensure that they are safe for treating patients.

activity Blood donation

This activity will enable you to learn more about the work of the Blood Transfusion Service (NIBTS) and why blood donation is important to help other people. This activity requires that you have internet access or your teacher may provide you with similar information.

1 Connect to the website for the Northern Ireland Blood Transfusion Service. Read the mission statement given at the site and explain what it means in your own words.

2 Navigate through the site to FAQs (frequently asked questions). List the basic requirements for becoming a blood donor.

3 What is donated blood tested for? Do these checks remove the viruses they are testing for?

4 Record the number of blood donors in Northern Ireland, and give two reasons why new donors are always needed.

5 List three complications of blood donation and make short notes on each one. Would these three problems make you less willing to become a blood donor? Explain your answer.

6 Even when people attend a donor session, they may be given a 'deferral'. Record the percentage of donors that are deferred and the reasons for deferral.

7 Find out what happens to blood after it is donated. Record what happens to the four parts of blood.

8 The people that receive donated blood are called 'recipients'. Record who receives red cells, platelets and plasma.

9 Apart from whole blood donation, in what other ways can you help the Blood Transfusion Service?

10 Navigate to the links webpage and click on the National Blood Service (for England and North Wales). Read some of the amazing stories from blood donors.

 11 As a class, debate this statement: *Blood donation is worthwhile*. You can use activity sheet *X7 Debating* to help you.

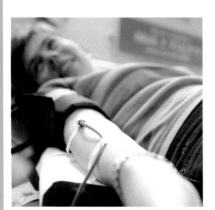

Figure 7 This person is donating blood.

extension activity Researching blood

1 Search the NBS website for England and North Wales to follow a virtual tour of a blood donation session. Record your feelings about blood donation after the tour. Do you think you would like to become a blood donor in the future? Give reasons for your answer.

2 Navigate to the screen: About the NBS. List the jobs that are available within the NBS. Record details about the opportunities that are available for scientists in the NBS.

---

1 **Explain why the heart is an unusual muscle.**
2 **Suggest ways of encouraging members of the public to become blood donors.**

→ 7.5 Protecting your heart

→ **In this unit we are learning:**

- to understand the effect of a blocked vessel on blood flow
- to measure pulse rate
- about the effect of exercise on heart rate
- about factors that increase and reduce the risk of heart disease (personal health).

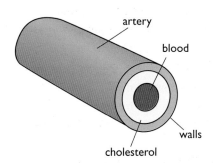

Figure 1 An artery showing how cholesterol can narrow it.

Heart health

The heart, like all of the organs of the body, must be treated properly to remain healthy. The heart is part of the **circulatory system** that also includes the blood and the blood vessels it travels through. To allow it to continuously pump the blood around the body the heart must receive a continuous supply of blood. If blood flow to the heart stops, then it stops beating.

If the **coronary artery**, a blood vessel that carries blood to the heart, is blocked, blood cannot reach the heart muscle. When we are born the coronary artery is clear. However, the coronary artery can be damaged by smoking, viruses, and a substance called **cholesterol** which is found in fatty foods. Damage to the artery can cause blood to clot inside the artery. Throughout history, doctors have used animals called leeches because they produce substances that prevent blood from clotting.

activity Using leeches

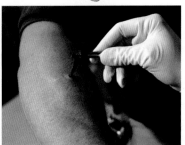

The use of leeches in medicine is known as hirudotherapy. Try to find out more about the use of leeches in medicine. Here are some questions that you might find answers to. When did this practice first begin? Why were they used in ancient times? What were they used to treat in the past? What are leeches used to treat today? What makes them popular today? Are there any hazards associated with them?

Figure 2 A leech on a patient's skin.

Figure 3 In this photo a portable defibrillator is being used.

One of the problems about a heart attack is that the ventricles flutter irregularly rather than beating properly. In the 1970s, Frank Pantridge, working at the Royal Victoria Hospital in Belfast, invented a portable **defibrillator**, a machine that gives the heart a short, sharp electric shock which is enough to get it beating properly again. This machine is small and light enough to be carried in an ambulance. Nowadays, many defibrillators are available in stations and airports, so that they can be used to help anyone who has a heart attack there.

practical activity Blocked vessel

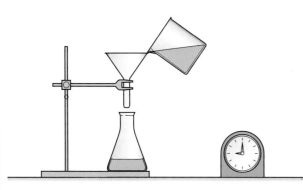

Figure 4

Sometimes a blood vessel can become partly blocked by a blood clot. This means the heart has to pump harder to force the blood through. In this activity you will examine how narrowing changes the rate that blood flows through a vessel. You should work with a partner.

1 In this part of the activity you will be given the following apparatus: a 100 ml measuring cylinder, a beaker, a retort stand and clamp, a timer, some coloured water, a 250 ml volumetric flask, a 250 ml conical flask and goggles. The two types of flask, one with a narrow and one with a wide neck, represent the blocked and clear arteries, which have different diameters.

2 Use the cylinder to measure 100 ml of coloured water and place in the beaker.

3 When one partner says 'go' and starts the timer, the other partner begins to pour the 100 ml of coloured water through the funnel and into the volumetric flask. The other partner stops the clock when all of the liquid has passed through the funnel. You should record the time taken in seconds.

4 Repeat Steps 2–3 twice more and work out the average time. Try to pour at the same speed each time and from the the same height.

5 Repeat Steps 2–4 using the conical flask.

6 Do you think it was important to repeat the activity three times using each flask? Explain your answer.

7 Now use the equation in the margin to work out the rate that water travelled into each flask.

8 Can you identify which model represents the normal and which the blocked vessel?

9 Explain why it puts extra strain on the heart if the coronary artery is blocked by cholesterol.

10 People sometimes suffer a heart attack when their blood becomes sticky. Plan an experiment using this equipment to investigate how blood becoming sticky would affect the rate of blood through the coronary vessel.

$$\text{Flow rate (ml/s)} = \frac{\text{volume (ml)}}{\text{time (s)}}$$

During exercise it is important that blood can travel even more quickly to your exercising muscles to deliver the glucose and oxygen gas needed to make energy by respiration. This means that your heart beats more quickly. This increase in heart rate is measured as **pulse**. Pulse rate is therefore a measure of how fast your heart is beating.

investigation

Measuring your pulse

In this activity you will investigate the effect of exercise on your pulse. You will then be able to determine whether an increase in breathing rate is accompanied by a change in heart rate. Normal pulse is around 65 to 70 beats per minute (bpm). Before you start the activity, predict the effect of exercise on your pulse. Do you expect it to increase or decrease?

1 Figure 5 shows you where to locate your pulse in your neck or wrist.
2 Count the number of times your heart beats for one minute, and record this. Repeat twice more and calculate the average (divide the total by three).
3 Walk on the spot for two minutes and record your pulse again.
4 Describe the effect exercise has on pulse.
5 Caffeine is thought to speed up the heart rate. Plan a fair test that could be used to compare the effect on pulse rate of a drink that contains caffeine with a caffeine-free drink. Show your plans to your teacher. If you have time try this test.

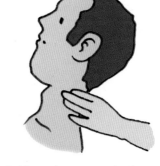

Figure 5 a Measuring your pulse in your wrist. **b** Measuring your pulse in your neck.

extension activity

Heart attack

Work together in a group of about six people. Your teacher will give you a set of activity cards. Each card shows a factor that either increases or decreases the risk of having a heart attack. It is your task to decide whether you think each factor increases or decreases the risk. All members of your group must agree with each of your answers. When you have finished, your teacher will correct your answers.

1 **Can you suggest why exercising might be dangerous for someone who has suffered heart damage?**
2 **Suggest why heart disease is more likely to occur in older people than young children.**

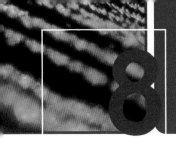

Let's find out about rocks

→ 8.1 Land of saints and scholars

→ **In this unit we are learning:**

- how environments vary
- how to measure and record environmental factors
- that organisms in a habitat adapt to seasonal change.

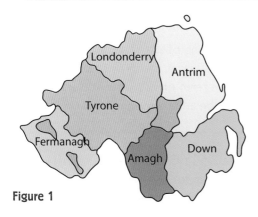

Figure 1

The island of Ireland has been described as 'a land of saints and scholars'. This description is of the people of Ireland, but what about the land itself? How would you describe the **landscape** of your county? Do you agree with the Northern Ireland Tourist Board (NITB) description? For example, County Antrim is described as '…home to the Giant's Causeway, the Glens of Antrim and Portrush, one of Northern Ireland's top seaside resorts'.

activity Describing my county

1 Use a search engine to find a tourism site for Northern Ireland that has a description of your county. For example, the website **www.n-irelandholidays.co.uk** provides a map with 'clickable' counties. How much of the description is about the landscape, and how much about the people? Would you change or add anything about the description of your county?

2 Draw a copy of Figure 1. Draw a bold line around your county and shade it in a colour of your choice.

3 Using ten words or less, write a slogan describing the landscape of your county.

4 Imagine that you have been commissioned by NITB to write a 100-word article describing your county. Word-process your article and include up to three images. Use your slogan from Step 3 as the title for your article.

Northern Ireland has different types of landscape. *Geography Pathways Y8* describes landscape as being *about the shape of the Earth, the plants that grow there, the soil, the mountains and the people too.* The shape of a landscape environment, the soil and plants are determined by the rock that lies underneath the area.

Figure 2 a This ash grows in a limestone area. **b** The oak tree grows in a basalt area. **c** Alders grow near water.

activity Environmental variables

Consider this statement.

Rock, soil and slope changes, among other environmental variables, have led to the creation of distinct types of woodland – for example, ashwoods in some of the limestone areas, native oakwoods on basalt, granite and other rock types – while many areas of mixed woodland are also found.

(Clue: Is Northern Ireland made up from just one type of rock? Look at Figure 5 on page 124 for ideas.)

1 Discuss with your partner the meaning of the word **variable**. Check your answer against the glossary at the back of this book.
2 What do you think is meant by the term **environmental variable**?
3 Can you explain how rocks might be an environmental variable?

Rocks can also determine the soil type in an environment, as soil is made up from the minerals that the rock contains, as well as water, air and organic matter (the living part). Your teacher will tell you where you can find a short animation called 'what is soil?'.

The water content of soil is important as it influences the type of plants that can grow in it. Alder trees like to grow on wet soils (see Figure 2).

activity Glorious mud

How might you measure the water content of soil? How could you compare soils from two or more different areas? What would you measure/change/keep the same?

activity Landscape and environment

The website **www.geographyinaction.co.uk** describes five different landscapes in Northern Ireland:
– Breen Wood, a deciduous forest
– Slemish, a volcanic plug
– Ballynahone, a peat bog
– White Rocks, chalk sea cliffs
– the Sperrins, Ordovician mountains.

Working in a group, choose two of these landscapes to compare and contrast, taking into account both the physical conditions and the different populations that live there. Make sure each person in the group has a job to do. Report your findings to the rest of the class. You can download activity sheet *X6 Thinking skills: Compare and contrast* to help you.

Figure 3 This weather station measures some abiotic factors.

Different landscapes have different environmental factors (or 'variables') and these factors in turn can affect the distribution of organisms in that place. There are two main kinds of environmental factor in any ecosystem, the living and non-living factors:

- **biotic factors**: the relationships between all the *living* things, for example, predation, competition between organisms, disease
- **abiotic factors**: these include all the physical and chemical (or *non-living*) factors in a habitat, for example, temperature, availability of light, rainfall (see Figure 3).

Plants and animals are adapted to live in their particular environment. They also adapt to seasonal changes in that environment (see Figure 4).

activity Measuring abiotic factors

In *Science Pathways Y8*, you looked at ways of estimating the numbers of living things in a habitat. In this activity you will measure some of the non-living or 'abiotic' factors in your school grounds.

In pairs, think of some of the physical factors that you might measure. How will you measure these factors? How will you record your results? Do you think that any of these factors change throughout the day (diurnal change)? What measurements could you take to find evidence for diurnal change? How could you use ICT to help you in this task?

Extend your thinking. You can use secondary sources to confirm some of your readings, for example: newspapers and weather stations.

Figure 4 a Tree in summer.   **b** Tree in winter.   **c** A bird nesting in a tree.   **d** Birds gathering to migrate.

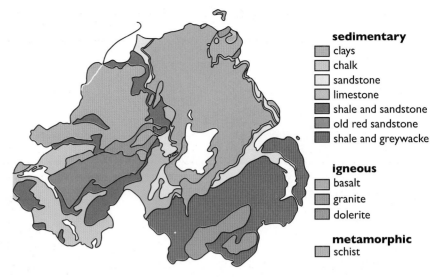

sedimentary
- clays
- chalk
- sandstone
- limestone
- shale and sandstone
- old red sandstone
- shale and greywacke

igneous
- basalt
- granite
- dolerite

metamorphic
- schist

Figure 5 Types of rock found in Northern Ireland.

Figure 6 Blanket bogs formed when Northern Ireland had high rainfall and humidity after the ice age.

The rocks underlying a landscape (see Figure 5) are also an 'environmental factor' as they are made up from different kinds of chemical compound. In Unit 8.2 you will learn about some of those rocks.

In Year 8 Geography you may have learned that rocks can be classified (or sorted) into three main types, depending on how they were formed: sedimentary, igneous and metamorphic. Rocks can inform us about past conditions in Northern Ireland (see Figure 6), as well as influencing the landscape of the present. You can find out more about this section from *A Story Through Time – The Formation of the Scenic Landscapes of Ireland (North)*, Patrick J McKeever, ISBN 1 899702 23 7.

1 **Explain how physical factors in an environment may change during summer and winter.**
2 **Explain how the plants and birds shown in Figure 4 are adapted to seasonal changes.**
3 **Think of two more examples of adaptations of organisms to seasonal change, one plant and one animal.**

→ 8.2 The rock cycle

→ **In this unit we are learning:**

■ that there are three types of rock, sedimentary, igneous and metamorphic
■ that the Earth's crust is constantly changing
■ that the material of the Earth's crust is constantly being recycled
■ that the size of crystals in rocks helps us to understand how the rocks were formed.

Figure 1 Giant's Causeway showing the columns of basalt.

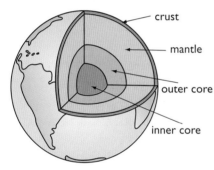

Figure 2 The structure of the Earth.

The Giant's Causeway is one of our main tourist attractions. It is made of columns of a volcanic rock called basalt. Geology, which includes the study of rocks, is very interesting, as it tells us about the foundation of our local landscape and the materials of some of our buildings. We have learned a lot about rocks from the study of volcanoes.

The Earth is thought to be about 4500 million years old. Much of the inside of the Earth (see Figure 2) is made of molten rock called magma. When a volcano erupts, this molten magma rises to the surface and then flows down the mountain as lava. The rate at which the lava cools affects the size of crystals in the rocks. You will discover that all rocks are linked in a constantly changing cycle.

There are three main types of rocks:
sedimentary, **igneous**, and **metamorphic**.

Figure 3 a Granite is an igneous rock. **b** Slate is a metamorphic rock. **c** Marble is a metamorphic rock. **d** Fossilised sponge embedded in chalk. **e** Sandstone is a sedimentary rock.

activity Examining rock samples

1 Use a magnifying glass to examine samples of rock. Look for crystals, different colours, different textures, fossils.
2 Discuss with your partner what you have found.
3 Draw pictures of what you see into your notebook.

Figure 4 The White Rocks are made of limestone.

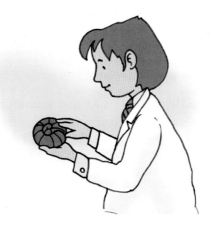

Figure 5 Fossils such as this may be found in sedimentary rocks.

Figure 6 The worktop is made from marble and the roof from slate.

Figure 7 The Mourne Mountains are made from granite.

Figure 8 Rathlin Island showing where the igneous basalt layer has flowed out of the Earth as lava, and been deposited on top of the earlier sedimentary chalk.

Sedimentary rocks are formed from layers of fine particles like sand or mud, or the bodies of small sea creatures, which get pressed together at the bottom of the sea or river bed. They may include fossils which are the remains of ancient life that got buried in the layers of sediment. The White Rocks (see Figure 4) are made of limestone. If you walk along the beach at Ballycastle, in County Antrim, and pick up some of the rocks which form pebbles there, you can find fossils called ammonites in the limestone rock. These were creatures that lived in the sea many years ago (see Figure 5).

Metamorphic rocks are formed when sedimentary rocks are subjected to extreme conditions of temperature and pressure. When the sedimentary rocks are buried deep below the sea they are under great pressure, and they are nearer to the centre of the Earth, which is very hot. Limestone becomes changed into a harder rock called marble. Mudstone is changed into slate. Marble and slate are described as metamorphic rocks. Both of these rocks can be used to make useful materials. For example, marble can be polished to make beautiful kitchen worktops, fireplaces, garden ornaments and furniture, and many other products. Slate is used to make attractive flooring and roofs for houses (see Figure 6).

Igneous rocks are formed when molten magma from under the Earth's surface flows out as lava (see Figure 8). The lava cools quickly, and has very tiny crystals like basalt. Sometimes the magma cools very slowly deep below the Earth's crust, and this kind of igneous rock has much larger crystals like granite which we can see in the Mourne Mountains (see Figure 7) where granite rocks are exposed at the surface. The next activity will help you to understand why crystals form in different sizes.

practical activity Making crystals of different sizes

Be safe: You must wear eye protection

You need:
- small blue crystals of copper sulphate
- the following apparatus: beaker, tripod and gauze, Bunsen burner, glass rod, filter funnel and paper, small conical flask, spatula, eye protection.

1 Put 50 cm³ of hot water into a small beaker.
2 Add copper sulphate crystals, and stir until these are dissolved.
3 Keep adding more copper sulphate crystals until no more will dissolve. The solution will be saturated.
4 Filter off the remaining crystals and leave half of the filtrate to cool slowly.
5 Put the other half into an evaporating dish and heat until 2/3 of the water has evaporated. Then remove it from the heat.
6 Compare the crystals formed from the two samples. What shape are the copper sulphate crystals in each dish?
7 Record your observations.

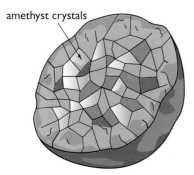

Figure 9 Amethyst crystals have formed in a ball of solid rock.

This experiment shows that larger crystals form when a substance cools slowly. Large diamond shaped crystals of copper sulphate can be grown by leaving a smaller crystal in a saturated solution for a few days.

When magma cools it contains bubbles of gas which can get trapped. These bubbles can form cavities inside a ball of solid rock. Sometimes very large crystals form in these cavities. They can become precious gemstones (see Figure 9).

The rock cycle

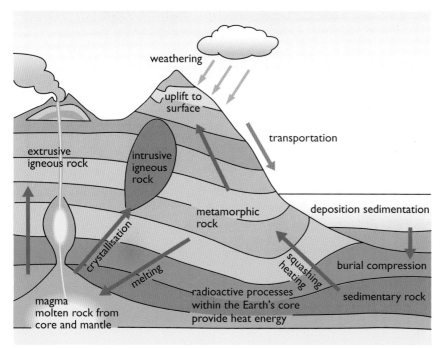

Figure 10 The rock cycle.

Figure 10 shows that existing mountain ranges are worn down by the weather and by erosion, to form tiny pieces of rock which form sediment. The sediment forms sedimentary rocks. Some of these are then changed to metamorphic rocks by extreme heat and pressure.

Beneath the surface of the Earth metamorphic rocks melt due to very high temperatures. They form molten rock called magma. Some of the magma moves upwards slowly and crystallises. During volcanic activity the magma reaches the surface and flows down the mountain forming igneous rocks. These then get exposed to weather and the cycle begins again.

practical activity

Hard rock

Igneous rock such as granite is used to make fireplaces, kitchen worktops, grave headstones, and water features in gardens. Other types of rock such as marble, slate (metamorphic rock) and sandstone (sedimentary rock) are also used.

1 Visit a local garden centre to find out what natural stones are used for garden landscaping.
2 Use a search engine to find out about an industry associated with local rocks and landscapes. What sort of work is involved? What special skills do you need? Where in Northern Ireland are granite products produced? Are they expensive? You may find the website **www.landscapeinstitute.org** useful.
3 Make a presentation about an industry which uses a local rock product.

---

1 **What are the three types of rock? Give examples of each type.**
2 **Where in Northern Ireland would you find: limestone, basalt, and granite?**
3 **What size of crystals do you find in granite? How is granite formed?**
4 **Draw a diagram of the rock cycle and explain how it works.**

→ 8.3 What can rocks tell us about our history?

→ **In this unit we are learning:**

- that we can find evidence for past conditions in Northern Ireland in the rocks that make up our landscape
- to use ICT to find out about life in the geological past
- to work in a group to research and manage information about a geological feature or mineral resource (economic awareness)
- about the work of geologists in the Geological Survey of Northern Ireland (employability).

Figure 1 Rocks are made from minerals, which are naturally occurring chemical elements or compounds. Granite is made up mostly of quartz, mica and feldspar.

Era	Period	Date
Paleozoic	Cambrian	600–500 million years ago
	Ordovician	500–440 million years ago
	Silurian	440–395 million years ago
	Devonian	395–345 million years ago
	Carboniferous	345–280 million years ago
	Permian	280–225 million years ago
Mesozoic	Triassic	225–190 million years ago
	Jurassic	190–136 million years ago
	Cretaceous	136–65 million years ago
Cenozoic	Tertiary	65–2 million years ago
	Quaternary	2 million years ago to present

Table 1 Geological periods.

In Unit 8.2 you learned about where rocks come from by studying the rock cycle. By looking at the rocks that make up Northern Ireland, geologists can find evidence for the geological history of our landscape, including where Northern Ireland was located in the past. Granite (see Figure 1) is found in the south east of Northern Ireland. In Geography you may have learned that the Earth's crust is made up of 'tectonic plates' that can move. Our small island has not always been situated at its present **latitude** on Earth, but has moved steadily northwards during hundreds of millions of years.

The most ancient rocks in Ireland, found in the Ox Mountains near Sligo, are thought to be about 1700 million years old. They are **metamorphic** rocks called gneiss, which geologists believe were formed when Ireland was part of a huge continent that lay near the southern pole! Geologists have devised a way of dividing up this huge time into periods as shown in Table 1. You can see that these periods last for many millions of years.

activity The geology detectives

Figure 2

Scientists who study rocks are called geologists. The Geological Survey of Northern Ireland (GSNI) employs many geologists in different roles.

1 In pairs, find out about some of the roles of geologists by going to **www.bgs.ac.uk/gsni** and clicking on 'About GSNI' and 'Services'. Write a 50-word summary about the work of geologists in GSNI.

2 In the Devonian Period, Ireland lay in the southern tropics and experienced a hot, arid climate. The north coast between Cushendall and Cushendun has evidence of this time in the sedimentary rocks there. Use a search engine to find four examples of plant and animal life in this period.

3 Upper and Lower Lough Erne lie on top of rocks that are mostly from the Carboniferous Period. These rocks were formed by sediments in a warm sea. Through time this rock changed to limestone, which contains the fossilised remains of plants and animals such as crinoids and coral that lived in the warm Carboniferous sea. Use a search engine to find out about crinoids.

4 In groups, research the features caused by the action of rainwater on limestone using Marble Arch Caves as an example. Present your results as a poster display or short talk. Make sure each person has a role to play.

5 The evaporation of a Triassic sea gave Carrickfergus its valuable deposits of rock salt (halite). When was the Triassic period? Find out about how much salt is mined at Carrickfergus by clicking **www.irishsaltmining.com**.

Element	Approximate % by mass
oxygen	46.6
silicon	27.7
aluminium	8.1
iron	5.0
calcium	3.6
sodium	2.8
potassium	2.6
magnesium	2.1
all others	1.5

Table 2 Elements in the Earth's crust.

The Mourne Mountain granites are among the youngest rocks in Northern Ireland; these **igneous** rocks are about 60 million years old. Granite is made up mostly from the minerals quartz (a compound containing silicon and oxygen), mica (containing silicon, oxygen and aluminium) and feldspar (containing the same elements as mica, but also containing potassium, or calcium and sodium). The most common elements that make up the Earth's crust are shown in Table 2.

1 **Which of the elements in Table 2 is important for the process of respiration?**

2 **Which of the elements shown in Table 2 is present in the rock salt mined at Carrickfergus?**

activity Mohs' scale

Find out about the link between Mohs' scale and minerals. Write a summary of about 50 words to explain Mohs' scale, including at least one diagram.

→ 8.4 Blueprint for a Solar System

> **→ In this unit we are learning:**
>
> - about the nebular theory of star formation
> - to identify energy changes in star formation
> - to make inferences by observing astronomical images.

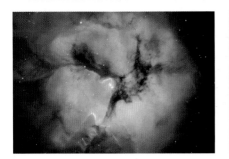

Figure 1 a M20 Triffid nebula 5200 ly from Earth.

b M16 Eagle nebula 7000 ly from Earth.

c Tarantula nebula 170 000 ly from Earth.

The speed of light is about 300 000 kilometres per second.

How are stars and planets made?

Stars, and the planets that orbit them, are made from huge clouds of dust and gas, called **nebulae** (singular: nebula) that can stretch from tens to hundreds of light years across in space. Some of these are shown in Figure 1.

It is difficult for us to comprehend these vast distances. In *Science Pathways Y8* you learned that a light year (abbreviation ly) is the distance light travels in one year. Remember that a light year is a measure of *distance*, not time.

---

activity **Light years**

1 With a partner, work out the distance light can travel in one year. *Hints* How many seconds are in a minute? How many minutes in one hour? How many hours in one day? How many days in one year? Compare the value you calculated with the other values calculated in the class. Did you all reach the same answer? Do you need to go back and check your calculation?

2 The Sun is about 150 million kilometres from Earth. How long does light take to reach us from the Sun? *Hints* How many zeros in 150 million?

You can see from the captions in Figure 1 that these nebulae lie many light years from Earth. This means that you are seeing light that left those nebulae many years ago. The Tarantula nebula lies in the Large Magellanic Cloud, a neighbouring galaxy to the Milky Way in which we live, so it is much further away than the other two nebulae (which are in our own galaxy). The image of M16, the Eagle nebula, was taken with the Faulkes telescope. The image has captured light that left the nebula 7000 years ago.

What elements are present in nebulae?

Most nebulae are composed mainly of hydrogen (90%), helium (almost 10%), and 0.1% of heavier elements such as carbon, nitrogen, magnesium, potassium, calcium, and iron. The heavy elements that make up the rocks of Earth came from the nebula from which our whole Solar System was formed, about 4.5 billion years ago. One of the reasons that scientists are interested in the composition of asteroids and comets is because this gives us information about the make-up of elements in the nebula that resulted in our Solar System.

practical activity   Recall gravitational potential energy

Hold a ball at arm's length above the ground. It has gravitational potential energy. Remember that gravity is a force that pulls everything back down to Earth. Drop the ball. As it falls to the ground it releases its gravitational potential energy, and this energy is transferred to different forms. For example, you hear sound when the ball hits the ground, and energy is transferred by friction to the air particles that it touches. Rub your hands together – what effect does friction have on the temperature of your hands?

In the same way, the particles in the nebula lose their gravitational potential energy as they fall together, and this is transferred to heat energy, so the temperature inside the ball of gas begins to rise. The temperature becomes so high in the centre that hydrogen gas particles, called hydrogen nuclei (singular: **nucleus**), fuse together and a totally new element is formed – helium.

When helium is formed from hydrogen nuclei, some of the mass is converted to an enormous amount of energy. The ball of gas begins to shine, and a star is born!

Look back at Unit 2.3 to see that mass is a form of energy.

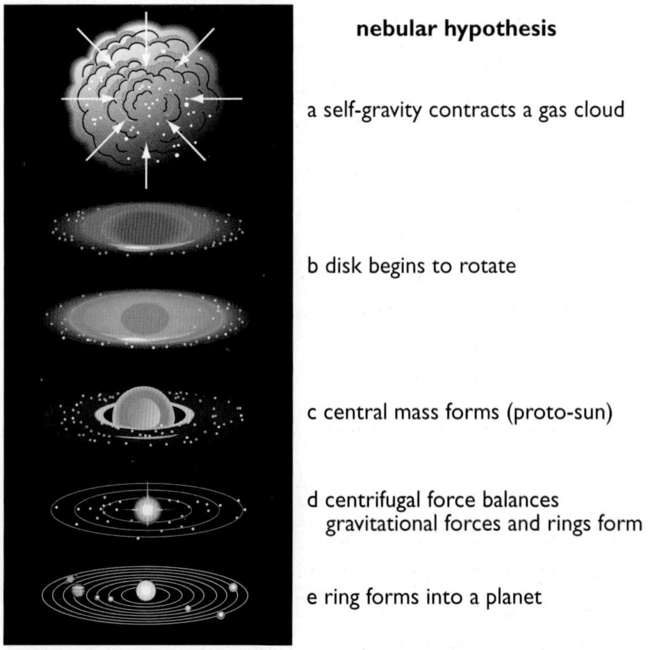

nebular hypothesis

a self-gravity contracts a gas cloud

b disk begins to rotate

c central mass forms (proto-sun)

d centrifugal force balances gravitational forces and rings form

e ring forms into a planet

Figure 2 The nebular theory.

The nebular theory of formation of the Solar System

This theory (see Figure 2) suggests that the particles of dust and gas (mostly hydrogen) that make up a nebula are given a 'push' from outside the nebula, perhaps from a supernova explosion (which you will learn about in the next unit).

This push causes some of the dust and hydrogen particles to fall towards each other and then gradually **gravity** takes over as more and more dust and gas particles collapse together. As the particles begin to coalesce (come together) the temperature inside the ball of gas and dust begins to increase. Why would this happen?

Gravity does not pull all the hydrogen particles in towards the centre of the star and cause its collapse, because the inward pull of gravity is balanced by an outward 'push' from the energy being released inside the star. As the dust cloud collapses in to form a star it also begins to rotate, and particles of dust caught in the rotating disc around the young star begin to come together to form **planets**.

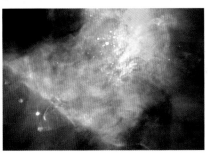

b Orion nebula.

The stars that you can see in the night sky belong to our own galaxy, and each one was born from a nebular cloud. You can see a very beautiful nebula when you look towards the constellation Orion (see Figure 3a). Orion's 'sword' is a vast cloud of dust and gas where new stars are being born. Astronomers sometimes refer to the Orion nebula (see Figure 3b) as a 'stellar nursery'!

Figure 3 a Orion constellation.

---

 activity Discovering Orion

Using a sky map, identify the constellation Orion. Try to observe the constellation in the night sky. To see the nebula better, look a little to one side of the 'sword' and you should have an improved view! This is because the light-sensitive cells at the back of your eyes that you use in the dark are not directly behind your pupil, but are just to one side of the centre of the retina.

1 What do you notice about the stars in the photograph of the Orion constellation in Figure 3a? Are they all the same? How are they different? From looking at this photograph what can you infer (which can mean hypothesise or theorise) about stars?

2 Use a search engine or the school library to find out more about the Orion constellation. What myths or stories lie behind the name of this constellation?

3 Using a sky map, make up two or three 'constellations' of your own by joining stars together with lines to make your own patterns. You can find star maps in many astronomy magazines. Display your constellations in class.

---

 activity Review

In this unit you have covered some material that may be new to you. Review your learning by drawing a sequence that explains the 'nebular theory' of the formation of the Solar System. Write some notes beside each drawing to explain what is happening, including any new ideas or terms that you have learned.

→ 8.5 What is science, anyway?

> → **In this unit we are learning:**
>
> ■ what science is
> ■ to understand how science works.

In Unit 8.4 you learned about the science of stars and planets, and how scientists have been using their own observations and complex instruments to find out about our Solar System and about stars and systems far beyond. This is the science of astronomy.

---

activity **About science**

You've been learning about science since primary school, or before. However, do you know what science is? Write down what you think is a good definition of science.

---

activity **What is science?**

1 Science is the systematic study of the nature and behaviour of the material and physical universe, based on observation, experiment and management.

2 Science is any body of knowledge organised in a systematic manner.

3 Science is what scientists do.

4 Science is knowing about biology, chemistry and physics.

5 Science is the organised building up and testing of evidence about the world of energy, materials, processes of life, and the environment, leading to tentative conclusions that can be tested experimentally.

Figure 1 Definitions of science.

Figure 1 shows some possible definitions that people have come up with when asked the question: *What is science, anyway?*

1 On your own, look at each of the five possible definitions. Two important words are 'systematic' and 'organised', because people in science need to organise their thoughts in a logical way, and to think clearly and systematically. Decide which definition is nearest to what you think science is.

2 In a small group:
   – share your definition, and decide which definition your group thinks is best
   – devise what you think might be a better definition.

3 Display the agreed definitions from each group and, as a class, decide a good definition for science.

4 Record this in your notebook.

You learned in *Science Pathways Y8* that many people think visually and learn more effectively from pictures rather than words. This is called visual learning. Figure 2 shows a possible definition of science in diagram form. Which of the definitions in Figure 1 is closest to this?

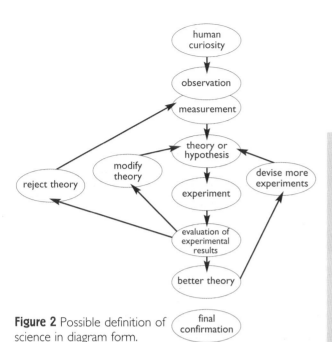

Figure 2 Possible definition of science in diagram form.

Figure 3 The apparent backward movement of a planet.

This picture is an idealised model of how thinking about science should work. However, science is carried out by real people, and seldom works in exactly this way. Often the steps are not taken in quite the order shown here, and the process may take hundreds of years before this pattern is obvious.

A long time ago people like the ancient Greek scientist <u>Aristotle</u> looked up at the stars and wondered (1) What are they? How did they get there? Why do they move the way they do? The Greeks noticed (2) that some of the stars, like Venus or Mars, didn't follow the same pattern as the others. They called these the wanderers, or planets. Some even appeared to go backwards (see Figure 3).

By the 16th century, astronomers like Tycho <u>Brahe</u> were able to work out the paths of the planets (3), but they couldn't understand why these paths were so irregular compared with the fixed stars. At that time most people thought that the Earth was the centre of the Universe, and that all the stars and planets travelled around the Earth. But Johannes <u>Kepler</u> said that the unusual paths of the planets could be understood if you thought of the Sun as the centre of the system, and that all the planets, including the Earth, went round the Sun. Kepler devised mathematical laws connecting the time a planet takes to go round the Sun with its distance from the Sun. However, he still couldn't explain why these laws worked.

In 1665 Isaac <u>Newton</u> was sitting in his garden in Lincolnshire when he saw an apple falling from a tree (or that's his story). He developed a theory that the apple falls because it is attracted to the Earth. All masses are attracted to all other masses, masses like apples and the Earth, or masses like the planets and the Sun. He did some sums and showed that his theory of gravitation could explain Kepler's observations and measurements (4). Lots of people like Henry <u>Cavendish</u> did experiments (5) and worked out their results (6) to improve Newton's theory (7), by making the figures more accurate.

But in 1905 Albert <u>Einstein</u> came up with the idea of relativity. This showed that there were others ways than Newton's theory to think about gravity: Newton's ideas weren't wrong, but Einstein improved on them (8). Scientists still don't know how gravity really works (9). So we can't confirm that the ideas of Newton or Einstein are final or complete; you might come up with a better idea if you continue with science after Key Stage 3.

Figure 4 The monument to Tycho Brahe and Johannes Kepler in Prague.

activity Steps in science

Read the story above. Each number (1) to (9) represents one of the ovals in Figure 2. Match each number to the appropriate word(s) in an oval. Explain why there isn't an arrow between the ovals for 'better theory' and 'final confirmation'.

→ 8.6 Star death

→ **In this unit we are learning:**

- about the life and death of stars
- how the death of stars leads to the elements that are part of our bodies
- to wonder at the Universe (spiritual awareness).

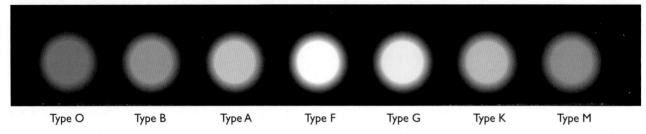

| Type O | Type B | Type A | Type F | Type G | Type K | Type M |

Figure 1 Spectral class types for stars.

Through the many years of human life on Earth, people have looked up in wonder and curiosity at the night sky. The stars appeared to be arranged in patterns that some people imagined as pictures in the sky. In Unit 8.4 you saw a photograph of the Orion constellation, which has stars of different colours and brightness. Some stars appear to be red and others white, or even blue-white.

The colour of a star gives us information about its age and surface temperature. Stars are classified by their colour into what are called 'spectral classes' (see Figure 1). The blue coloured type O stars are the hottest and red type M the coolest. Can you find a red star in Orion? The star Betelgeuse is a red 'supergiant' star. Astronomers remember this classification by the mnemonic *O be a fine girl, kiss me*. Our own star, the Sun, is a type G, a yellow star. Like people and animals, stars are born, become middle-aged and eventually die: stars have a life cycle that is just as inevitable as our own, so they do not stay the same for ever.

front legs break through

eggs

adult frog

tadpole with all legs

metamorph

tadpole

Figure 2 Stages in the life cycle of a frog.

 activity Sequencing life cycles

Look at the images shown in Figure 2. Put the stages into the correct sequence to show the progression of the life cycle.

One big difference between a star life cycle and a human life cycle is that stars can live for billions of years! A billion is a 1 with *nine* zeros after it (or, a thousand million)! In *Science Pathways Y8* you learned about the 'Big Bang' that created our universe. In the first few minutes of the Big Bang only three elements were created, the main one being hydrogen. If that is so, where did all the rest of the elements come from?

Scientists have estimated that our own Sun is now about 4.5 billion years old, and is about half-way through its life cycle. We have looked in Unit 8.4 at the theory that our own Sun was 'born' from a nebula of dust and gas, and we saw images of some nebulae in the Milky Way galaxy. We can also find images that provide evidence of other stages in a star's life cycle, even star death.

Star death is not a bad thing for a galaxy: it is actually a wonderfully creative event that can bring diversity by enriching space with new elements. Scientists believe that the heavier elements like carbon, nitrogen and oxygen that make up much of the rocks and organisms on Earth were formed inside stars that exploded and released the elements back into space. These elements then became part of another nebula. The carbon in your body was billions of years in the making; you are made of star stuff!

The way that a star dies depends on its original mass. We refer to our own Sun as having 'one solar mass' and compare other stars to it. Stars that are about the same mass as our Sun have a different life cycle compared with stars that are much more massive.

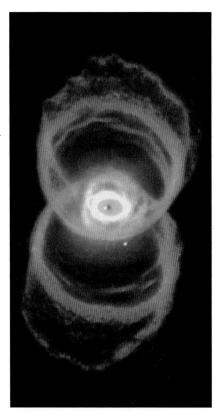

Figure 3 The hourglass nebula.

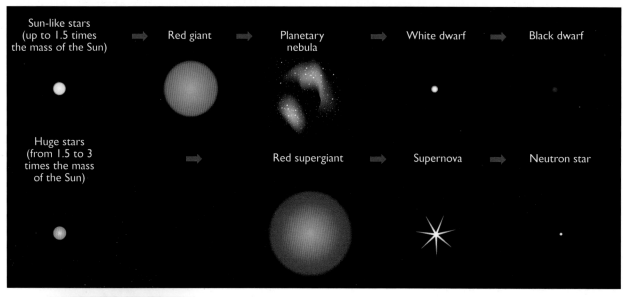

Figure 4 The life cycle of stars.

The different sizes of star also create different elements during their lifetime. We learned that the Sun produces helium when hydrogen nuclei fuse together. When the hydrogen fuel of a star is used up, helium nuclei are then fused together. Small stars like our Sun fuse helium to create carbon and nitrogen towards the end of their lives. During this time the temperature of the star decreases, which has two results that can be observed by telescopes. The star expands and changes colour as it cools, forming a 'red giant'.

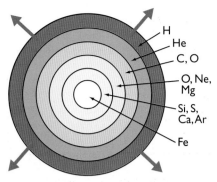

Figure 5 'Onion shell' model of a massive star.

Larger stars can maintain much hotter temperatures than smaller ones, so they can fuse helium to form such elements as oxygen and magnesium while also creating carbon. These massive stars can forge successively heavier elements up to iron. Massive stars become red 'supergiants' at the end of their life cycle. The structure of these massive stars is described as an 'onion shell', with different elements at different layers around the core of the star.

All these different elements are released into space when the stars eventually die. Small stars blow off their outer shells to form a 'planetary nebula', while more massive stars end their lives in a supernova explosion (which produces elements heavier than iron) and may even form a 'black hole'.

---

activity Researching star life cycles

Use a search engine to find different images of stages in a star's life cycle and create a PowerPoint slide show.

---

investigation How do we know what elements are in stars?

In *Science Pathways Y8* (Chapter 1), you learned about using flame tests to see what elements were in a powder. Hot gases can give out coloured light too. You are aware of the different colours in fluorescent lighting: pink for neon, yellow for sodium and so on. The coloured light emitted by hot gases can be used to identify elements in stars. Find out what colours are produced by the following gases: hydrogen, helium, nitrogen, oxygen.

Figure 6 The flame test.

---

activity Researching the aurora borealis

If you have time, search the internet for information on the *aurora borealis* or northern lights.

→ 8.7 Using robotic telescopes

→ In this unit we are learning:

- that we can use ICT to control telescopes that are very distant from Northern Ireland
- about the different types of data that can be accessed from internet websites
- about the roles of astronomers in the Faulkes Telescope team (employability).

By looking at the night sky we can distinguish different constellations of stars. We can also observe the various phases of the lunar cycle.

1 This is designed to review your learning from last year. Can you remember the phases of the Moon? Put the following phases into the correct sequence, beginning and ending with a full Moon: waxing crescent, waning crescent, waxing gibbous, waning gibbous, first quarter, last quarter, new Moon, full Moon.

Figure 1 Jupiter and its four largest moons.

We can use binoculars to give us more detail of the sky at night. For example, if you observe the planet Jupiter with binoculars, you can see its four major satellites, or moons: Io, Europa, Ganymede and Callisto.

By plotting the positions of Jupiter's moons over a series of evenings, you can identify each moon by its location. Astronomy magazines often publish the orbits of its moons, so this can help you confirm your identification. By observing Jupiter in this way you are following in the footsteps of Galileo Galilei, who in 1610 made drawings and notes about his study of Jupiter's moons. These observations provided evidence that overturned the previously held belief that all objects in the night sky orbited the Earth, as the moons were quite clearly orbiting the planet Jupiter. Your teacher will give you a website where you can find an animation of the moons.

Galileo's telescope was one that he made himself. Today, pupils from schools in Northern Ireland can use multi-million pound research telescopes located in different places around the world, such as the Faulkes telescopes in Hawaii. The telescopes can be booked and controlled from your school's computer network, allowing you to see far beyond the moons of Jupiter, to nebulae and stars far away from our own Solar System.

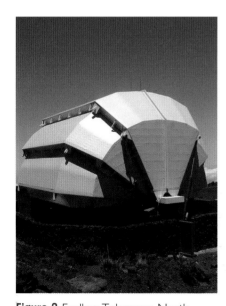

Figure 2 Faulkes Telescope North (FTN).

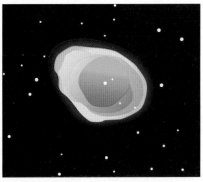

Figure 3 The ring nebula imaged by Glenlola Collegiate School.

Some pupils have already used the telescope to capture their own images. Local pupils imaged the 'Ring Nebula' using the Faulkes Telescope North (FTN). The girls were given 29 minutes on the telescope and used the time to make the beautiful coloured image shown in Figure 3.

When taking images with the telescope you must decide on appropriate exposure times and also which filters to use. The nebula was imaged using three different filters: red, green and blue, each with an exposure time of 60 seconds. The Faulkes telescope website **www.faulkes-telescope.com**, gives information and advice about using the telescope, including exposure times and use of filters.

activity ## The Hubble classification of galaxies

In this activity you will use different types of data from the Faulkes telescope website to review the way that galaxies are classified. Work in small groups to research and carry out this activity, making sure that everyone knows exactly what their job is within the group. You will need to download information about the Hubble classification of galaxies as well as some images of individual galaxies.

Figure 4 A spiral galaxy.

1 Go to **www.faulkes-telescope.com** and type 'classification of galaxies' into the search box. You will be guided to a page entitled 'Measuring and classifying galaxies'. From this page you can access a document outlining the Hubble Classification of galaxies.

You can find additional activities, including instructions which allow you to take your own images using the Faulkes telescope if your teacher has registered as a user.

2 Go to: **www.faulkes-telescope.com/image_gallery**. Using the images stored in the image gallery, prepare a poster explaining the Hubble classification of galaxies.

Many members of the Faulkes Telescope (FT) team are astronomers, but not everyone. Hayley is an astronomer with a special interest in cosmic dust and supernovae. You can find out about the other members of the Faulkes Telescope team on the website.

Figure 5 Hayley.

9 The brain and thinking

→ ## 9.1 Connecting the parts of my brain

→ **In this unit we are learning:**

- more about the structure and functions of the brain
- to communicate information effectively (media awareness)
- about movements that improve our ability to learn information (personal health).

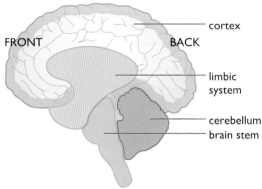

Figure 1 Parts of the brain.

What are the functions of the areas of the brain?

You were introduced to the main parts of your brain in *Science Pathways Y8* (Unit 10.4). These are shown in Figure 1, and include the cortex (which controls our conscious thoughts), the limbic system (responsible for emotions, learning and memory), the cerebellum (which controls our movements), and the brain stem (which controls automatic actions like breathing and running from danger).

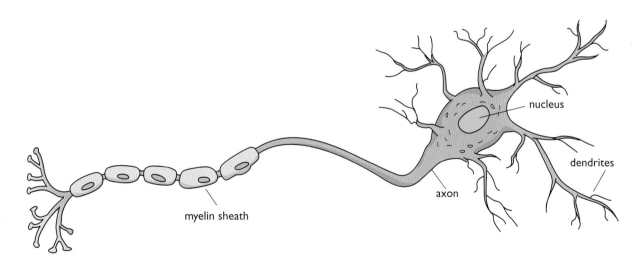

Figure 2 A neuron.

The central nervous system includes your brain and the spinal cord, which exchanges messages with the rest of your body. The parts of your brain are connected by **neurons**, which are specialised nerve cells that carry electrical messages, and connect the parts of the nervous system together. As you can see from Figure 2, neurons have the cell features you learned about last year, like the nucleus. However they also have long **axons**, which reach out to other neurons. These can pass electrical signals from one neuron to many others.

activity Details about the brain

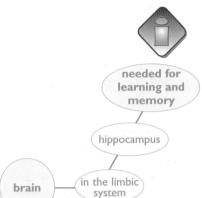

By the end of this activity you will have a greater understanding of the structure and functions of the main areas of your brain. You do not need to learn this information but it is useful to be familiar with these areas. After all, they're all inside your head.

1 Use books or a search engine to find a simple diagram that shows the structure of the brain. Find the following areas of the limbic system: the **hippocampus**, the **hypothalamus**, the **thalamus**, the **pons area**, the **amygdala**, the **medulla** and the **mid brain**.
2 Draw a simple diagram of the brain in your workbook.
3 Create a spray diagram to record the positions of the areas printed in bold in Step 1. This is started for you in Figure 3. Record some simple details about these brain areas including the function they perform. Add this information to your spray diagram.

Figure 3 A simplified structure of part of the brain.

activity Brain cards

Your teacher will organise you into groups, and give each member of the group a card. One side of the card contains a question about the brain, and there is an answer to a different question on the other side. The person with the starter question reads it. The person who thinks he has the correct answer reads this answer, and then, if the answer is correct, flips over the card and reads his question. This continues until the final answer is obtained. If anyone makes a mistake you must start again.

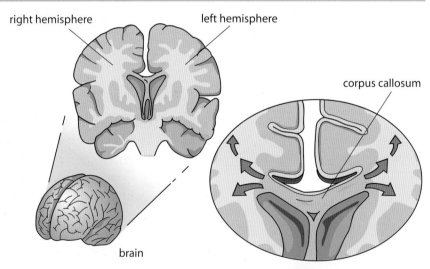

Figure 4

You already know that the limbic system and cortex of your brain are divided into two sections, called **hemispheres**, and each hemisphere has its own amygdala and hippocampus, and so on. However, did you know that the muscles on either side of your body are controlled by the opposite side of your brain? The right hemisphere of the brain controls the muscles on the left side of your body and the left hemisphere controls the muscles on the right. Information from the sense organs generally also crosses to the opposite sides of the brain.

This was discovered by doctors studying patients whose brain hemispheres were separated in two. In these patients the **corpus callosum**, which is a band of neurons that connects the right and left hemispheres of the brain, had been damaged. In the past, much information about the structure and operation of the brain has been discovered by scientists studying the behaviour of people whose brains were damaged.

Horrible Accident. - As Phineas P. Gage, a foreman on the railroad in Cavendish, was yesterday engaged in tampkin for a blast, the powder exploded, carrying an iron instrument through his head an inch and a fourth in circumference, and three feet and eight inches in length, which he was using at the time. The iron entered on the side of his face, shattering the upper jaw, and passing back of the left eye, and out at the top of the head.

The most singular circumstance connected with this melancholy affair is, that he was alive at two o'clock this afternoon, and in full possession of his reason, and free from pain. Ludlow, Vt., Union.

Figure 5 News report about Phineas Gage.

The damaged brain in action

In 1848 Phineas P Gage, working on railway construction in Vermont, was caught in a dynamite explosion. An iron bolt, over 1 metre long and 30 mm in diameter, ploughed through his cheek and the cortex region of his brain. Phineas survived, but his personality was severely changed: he went from being a pleasant easy-going man to an unpleasant alcoholic. From this, scientists concluded that the cortex area of the brain was involved in controlling personality.

Since then we have learned more about the nerve connections across the brain from examining live patients with brain damage, and from post mortems, which are examinations of parts of the body after death. This has helped to identify the effects of brain damage, and to link the symptoms of disease with damaged areas of the brain. This information is used to work out how normal, live undamaged brains operate.

activity Newspaper reporter

In this activity you are asked to write a newspaper article of about 200 words, starting with Phineas Gage's accident and brain damage. There are many references to Phineas Gage on the internet. You must decide who your target audience is, and you should illustrate your work with a picture of Phineas Gage.

Also find out about and include the most recent developments in technology that have enabled scientists to find out more about the brain. These may focus on the different types of brain scan that can be performed.

You have learned that your cortex and limbic system are divided into right and left brain hemispheres. In the seventeenth century the French scientist, Rene Descartes, suggested that the brain functions properly only when the two hemispheres are working together. In 1969 the American Paul Dennison showed that physical exercises improve communication between the right and left brain hemispheres. He developed a series of controlled, physical movements he called 'brain gym'. These movements can help to improve your concentration, your memory, your body movements and your language skills. These activities have been shown to greatly improve the brain functions of the people that were studied for their effects.

How can movement improve your learning?

Your ability to think and to learn will improve when the sides of your brain are connected in a balanced way. This means that if you improve the nerve connections between the two sides of the brain, you improve your ability to learn. These activities help to develop the nerve pathways across the brain. You should find the activities are easy to learn, take little time and do not require any equipment.

activity Connecting right and left

Be safe: You must have permission from your parent or carer before you take part in Step 5

In this activity you will examine the effect of performing the activities on your ability to spell some words that you might meet in science.

1 Your teacher will give you a list of ten scientific words. You will have two minutes to learn how to spell these words.
2 When two minutes have passed you will be given a spelling test.
3 Mark your answers out of a score of ten.
4 Calculate an average for the scores of your class.
5 Now complete this activity in a standing position:
   - raise your right knee and at the same time touch your knee using your left hand
   - repeat this activity using your right hand to touch your left knee as you raise it.
   You should imagine that you are marching. Continue the activity for two minutes.
6 You will be given a further list of ten spellings and should repeat Steps 1 to 3 above.
7 Compare the results for the class before and after the exercise. Did the average score change? Write a statement to describe any change that you observed.
8 Draw a bar chart to display the results from the class before and after the activity.

1 **Gary holds a tennis racquet in his left hand. Which side of his brain co-ordinates his movements when he is playing tennis? Explain your answer.**
2 **State how the two sides of the brain are connected together and suggest why this is important.**

9.2 How can I develop my critical thinking?

→ **In this unit we are learning:**

- to be aware of the stages that take place during learning
- to understand why learning is important (personal understanding)
- that many important discoveries were made by asking questions (cultural understanding)
- how science investigation works (cultural understanding)
- to develop our thinking skills.

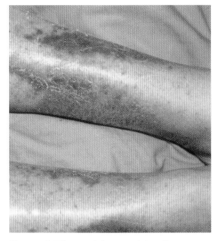

Figure 1 These shins are bleeding as a result of scurvy.

Figure 2 Dr James Lind.

What do I need to learn, and why is learning important?

Scientists are people who observe events, make measurements, and ask questions about how and why things happen. They try to find answers to their questions by carrying out investigations and experiments. They examine the results of their experiments to explain why things happen in the way they do.

By reflecting on their results scientists can suggest improvements or propose new ideas. Sometimes these improvements arise when they question ideas that have been accepted for a long time. The often fatal disease of scurvy, for example, was common among sailors who had been on long voyages, and did not have a fresh supply of fruit and vegetables. Scientists like the French explorer Jacques Cartier in 1536 treated scurvy by boiling the needles of a cedar tree to make a tea. (Do <u>not</u> try this yourself!) It worked, but at the time he did not realise that this tea contained a large amount of **vitamin C**.

It was not until 1747 that Dr James Lind showed that scurvy could be treated by adding citrus fruits to the diet. He was the first scientist to perform a controlled trial. He gave some sailors one or two oranges a day. As a result these sailors did not develop scurvy but others, who were not given any oranges, did. Even so, some people did not believe Lind's findings. They claimed that good hygiene was more important than citrus fruit, so many sailors continued to suffer from scurvy.

Following the discovery of vitamins in 1912, vitamin C was identified by the Hungarian scientists Joseph L Svirbely and Albert Szent-Györgyi between 1928 and 1933. Scurvy can now be prevented because these scientists had discovered that it is caused by a deficiency of the nutrient vitamin C in the diet. Their work protects people today from a fatal illness.

In school science there are problems you will be asked to investigate. You will be required to plan and carry out experiments. By examining your results you will be able to make informed choices, take decisions, and solve problems. This type of activity allows you to think about why things happen as they do, and to use your results and conclusions to confirm or disagree with your ideas and predictions. You can then correct your previous ideas.

Media sources present ideas about the types of food we should eat to maintain and improve our health. Health experts recommend that we should eat five portions of fruit and vegetables daily. These foods are a rich source of vitamin C, which has many roles in the body, in particular as an **antioxidant**. As you will find out later in this unit, antioxidants are believed to help in the fight against **cancer**.

It is easy to calculate how much vitamin C is present in fruit and vegetables. If iodine is added to starchy foods that contain vitamin C, the iodine binds with vitamin C. This means that more iodine can be added to foods that contain a lot of vitamin C before the iodine changes colour and a blue–black colour appears. By comparing the amount of iodine that can be added before the blue–black colour appears, those foods that have the most vitamin C present can be identified (see Figure 3).

Figure 3 Testing for starch using iodine.

investigation

Vitamin C problem solving

This activity will help to develop your problem solving thinking skills. It has been divided into four sections.

Part 1: Finding out about Vitamin C
This first section will develop your ability to research a particular topic.

1 Find out how the role of this nutrient was discovered.
   Use a search engine to research the history of vitamin C, particularly the trials carried out by James Lind and the work of Joseph L Svirbely and Albert Szent-Györgyi.
2 Describe all the symptoms that are caused by a deficiency of vitamin C.
2 Before starting the practical investigation, use books, the internet or other sources to record the amount of vitamin C in 100 g of each of these foods; oranges, grapefruits, blackcurrants, apples.

Part 2: Planning the investigation
You will be given a selection of fruit or fruit juices to investigate. Your aim in this part of the activity is to plan an investigation to enable you to identify foods that are rich sources of vitamin C. You should work in a group of about four people. Here are some guidelines to help you make your plan.

1 You will be given types of fruit or fruit juice such as orange, grapefruit, blackcurrant and apple.
2 The following apparatus will be available to choose from: a pestle and mortar, test tubes, test tube rack, 10 ml measuring cylinders, spatula, filter paper, filter funnel, conical flask, 30 ml of starch solution, iodine solution, droppers.

Be safe: You must wear eye protection

Look back to Unit 4.3 to see what is meant by a risk assessment.

3   Make a plan that will enable you to investigate which of the foods are the best sources of vitamin C. It is best to investigate the level of vitamin C in solutions. Remember to plan a fair test. Carry out a risk assessment to identify any safety rules you will have to obey.

4   When you have created your plan show it to your teacher. Your teacher will discuss the plans from each group with the class, to agree a common method that the entire class can follow.

5   Make a prediction about which of the foods has the greatest amount of vitamin C. Use these results to rank the foods in order from those that contain the greatest to the least amounts of vitamin C.

6   Now carry out the activity and record your results carefully.

Part 3: What do your results tell you?

Now that you have carried out the investigation you can use your results to identify the best food sources of vitamin C.

1   Rank the four types of juice in order for the best source of vitamin C.

2   Did the results agree with your predictions? Suggest how you could make your results more accurate.

3   Cooking is known to affect the levels of the nutrient in foods. Repeat the practical part of the activity but this time place each of the solutions in a water bath of boiling water for five minutes before adding iodine. (See Figure 4.)

4   Rank the foods again in order from the best to the worst source of vitamin C.

5   What effect did heating the foods have on the amount of nutrient they contained?

6   Was there any change in the rank order of the foods? What change if any was shown?

7   Explain why your results are important and suggest who might be interested in finding out these results.

8   Design a leaflet to alert cooks to your findings.

9   Imagine you wanted to make a variety of fruit jam that has the highest level of vitamin C. Which of the fruits would you choose? Explain your answer.

Figure 4 Warming the solutions in a water bath.

Part 4: Why are these results important?

In the final part of this activity you are asked to think about why your results are important.

1   Refer back to the food samples you investigated. Which of the foods would have been the most suitable for eighteenth-century sailors? Explain how you decided.

2   The amount of vitamin C in your body is particularly interesting because it is an antioxidant. Find out why antioxidants are important in preventing cancer.

3   Smokers may contain a lower level of vitamin C in their blood than non-smokers. Biomedical scientists can measure how much vitamin C there is in samples of blood.

Figure 5 Fresh fruit and vegetables contain vitamin C.

You should find out whether it is possible to raise the level of vitamin C in people with low levels by giving them some tablets that contain vitamin C. Remember that, if some people in the study do not receive tablets with vitamin C, you will have created a controlled trial just like James Lind.

1 Explain why it is important to ask questions in science.
2 Sometimes the results of experiments do not agree with your initial ideas. Does this mean that your ideas are wrong? Explain your answer.
3 Suggest why it is important to carry out experiments more than once, rather than using your first results.

→ 9.3 All right, all left, or somewhere in-between?

→ **In this unit we are learning:**

- that the two hemispheres of the brain perform different tasks
- to investigate whether people use more of one side of their brain than the other
- to learn about the activities of either brain hemisphere.

As you have learned in Unit 9.1, the cortex and limbic system in your brain are divided into two sides, the left and right hemispheres. As you know, the right hemisphere of the brain controls the muscles on the left side of your body and vice versa. Most people use the muscles and senses on one side of their bodies more than the other. You may prefer to use one hand in particular, left or right, to write with. Some people use both hands equally to perform many tasks: they are called ambidextrous.

Figure 1 Monica Seles is left handed.

practical activity

Mainly left or right?

This activity will identify whether you, and members of your class, use one side of your body more than the other.

Figure 2 Which hand do you write with?

1 Which hand do you write with? Record your response in your workbook. Which side of the brain do you think controlled this movement?
2 Place a coin on the floor in front of you. Step forward onto the coin. Which foot did you use? Did you use the same side of your body you used for Task 1? Record your response.
3 Place a small object in a box and shake it. To hear the noise of the rattle more clearly, you may have to place the box close to one ear. Which side of your head did you place next to the box? Record your response.
4 Roll a piece of paper into a tube. Place the tube close to one eye to look at a distant object. Record your response. Which eye did you use to look through the tube?
5 Create a blank table for recording the results for Tasks 1 to 4 for the members of your class.
6 Collect the results from the other members of your class.
7 About 90% of the population is thought to prefer using their right hand to perform tasks. Calculate the percentage of your class who are right-handed. Compare the results from the class with the population.
8 Calculate the percentage of your class who use the right sides of their bodies for the other three tasks. Your teacher will give you general figures for Tasks 2 to 4, so that you can compare your class results with those of the general population. Write a sentence to compare these results with the general population figure.

Figure 3 Edward Wilson.

Are male and female brains different?

You learned in Year 8 about differences between males and females. For hundreds of years scientists have searched for differences between the brains of males and females, possibly in brain structure. Edward Wilson, an American sociobiologist, has suggested that in general females have better verbal (spoken) and social skills. They are thought to be better at performing more than one activity at the same time: this is called multi-tasking. Males however, are considered better at mathematical calculations, and more able to visualise problems in three dimensions (spatial skills).

investigation Male brains and female brains

1 Do you think that males are more likely than females to use the left side of their brain? Explain your answer.
2 Plan an investigation that would enable you to answer this question. (Questionnaires are available on the internet to identify whether people use one side of their brain more than the other – or perhaps you could make your own.)
3 How many people would you survey?
4 How would you present your results?
5 Once you have shown your plans to your teacher, carry out your planned investigation.
6 Did you obtain the results that you expected? Write a statement to describe what your results show.

extension activity Edward Wilson

Use books or the internet to find out more about the work of Edward O. Wilson. You may find activity sheet *XI Famous scientist* useful here.

What do the right and left hemispheres of the brain do?

Each side of the brain controls certain behaviour and deals with different information from the surroundings. The **right hemisphere** deals mainly with spatial abilities, face recognition, visual images and music. It is where our imagination and artistic skills, humour and emotions are mainly controlled.

In general, most people who use the right hemisphere first take in all the information, look at the 'big picture', then examine the details. They prefer to jump about from task to task before completing a single task. They like hands-on activities and active learning. They may become confused when they are speaking, and prefer drawing exercises.

The **left hemisphere** is more responsible for calculations, mathematics and logic ability. This side of the brain prefers detailed information and problem-solving tasks. It deals best with difficult tasks with many steps. People who use the left hemisphere most take pieces of information and put them in order to create an entire picture. They like to make lists, and can easily learn lists of information. They can use symbols and formulae, and use words easily to explain what they want.

activity · What do the two sides of the brain do?

This activity asks you to identify the differences between the right and left hemispheres of the brain.

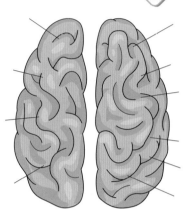

Figure 4

1 From the passage above, create a list of the features that could be used to identify people who prefer to use the right side or the left side of their brain.

2 Copy the pictures of the two halves of the brain shown in Figure 4. Add labels where indicated to display the activities that are performed by the two sides of the brain.

3 Sort the list of statements below into those that identify people who prefer to use mostly the right or left side of the brain. People who:

  a prefer to learn dance steps by walking step-by-step through the movements

  b have a place for objects and always put them in their places

  c prefer to draw pictures rather than write

  d do not like art as a school subject

  e can easily remember people's names but not their faces

  f have a workplace that is usually cluttered and untidy

  g rarely hand in their school projects on time

  h prefer to learn while sitting straight up, rather than slouching back.

1 Why would it would be incorrect to describe yourself to be only right-brained or left-brained?

2 a What term is used to describe someone who uses both hands equally?

  b What does this suggest about which side of the brain they are most likely to use?

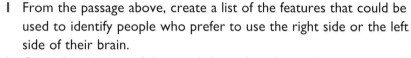

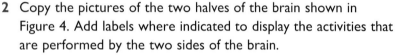

→ 9.4 Learning and memory

The brain and thinking

→ In this unit we are learning:

- to understand what is meant by memory and the different types of memory
- to appreciate that a huge number of neuron connections is possible
- to investigate the Stroop effect.

What is memory?

Memory is the ability to store information and experiences in your brain, through strengthening your neuron connections. There are two general types of memory, **short-term memory** and **long-term memory**. Short-term memory is sometimes called active memory or **working memory**.

In your short-term memory, information is stored for a short period of time only, between 30 and 60 seconds, for example remembering a telephone number, which you then forget. The information enters your brain through one of the senses, or is recalled from long-term memory. You use this type of working memory when solving a mathematical problem.

Long-term memory lasts between 30 seconds and a lifetime. There are three main types of long-term memory, **episodic memory**, **semantic memory** and **procedural memory**. Episodic memory refers to remembering personal experiences, such as your ninth birthday party. Semantic memory enables you to consciously recall information such as facts and figures, information about the outside world and how to find your way home from school. Procedural memory allows you to remember skills that you have learned, like riding a bicycle.

activity Do you remember?

In this activity you will identify the different types of memory used in a variety of situations.

1 Identify the type of memory used in each of the following activities by choosing from: active or working, episodic, semantic and procedural.
   a Knowing how to ride a bicycle.
   b Recognising your sister's friend.
   c Listing the presents you received last Christmas.
   d Working out the answer to a sum.
   e Distinguishing a fly from a spider.
   f Knowing how to use your Playstation.
   g Telling someone the number of your mobile phone.
2 Write a sentence to explain each of the types of memory listed above. Swap your list with a partner and ask her to identify each type of memory from your descriptions. Agree correct answers between you.

152

How is memory created?

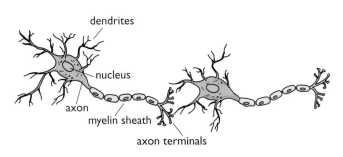

dendrites

nucleus

axon

myelin sheath

axon terminals

Figure 1 Neurons.

Short-term memory is produced when a nerve impulse travels from one nerve cell or **neuron** in your brain to others. This new link between the neurons is only temporary. This nerve impulse must be connected onto an existing pathway of nerve impulses that had been formed in the brain at an earlier time. If this new link formed between the nerve cells is repeated many times then a long-term memory will be created. Long term memories are formed by a permanent pathway between nerve cells or neurons in your brain that changes the structure of their connections. This is why you find it easier to remember the spelling of science words when you repeat them over and over.

You will probably have difficulty remembering anything that you find boring. You remember the names of your friends, but have trouble with a shopping list. Your memory is stronger if it is linked to your emotions. It is easier to commit information to long-term memory if it makes you feel happy or sad. If you were asked what your first memory is, it is probably some event that caused you to feel one of these emotions.

activity Making connections

You have approximately 10^{11} (a hundred thousand million) nerve cells, or neurons, with up to 10^{15} (a thousand million million) connections. This means that your brain could never become overcrowded with information. The following activity will help you to understand how so many connections are possible.

1 Draw ten dots, each of a different colour, down the left side of a page in your workbook. Skip a line between every dot. Draw a further ten dots opposite this line on the right side of your workbook.
2 Draw a line from the one dot to each of the other nine dots.
3 Move to the second dot and repeat Step 2 for all nine other dots.
4 How many connections have you made?
5 Move to the third dot and repeat Step 2 for all nine other dots.
6 How many connections have you made now?

   The formula for this is that the total number of connections is $\frac{1}{2}N(N-1)$ where N is the number of dots. How many connections could you make with 100 dots? Think how many connections you might make with 10^{11} neurons!

You may have found that you use one side of your brain more than the other. However, communication between many areas of your brain is essential for it to function effectively. In fact when you are reading the words of this book, your mid-brain is responsible for sight, while the cerebellum of your brain is controlling your eye movements. This means that the areas of your brain must communicate with each other to process information. In 1935, an American psychologist, John Ridley Stroop, demonstrated a delay in processing information that resulted in a slower reaction time (the **Stroop effect**).

RED ORANGE GREEN BROWN PINK	GREEN BLUE YELLOW RED YELLOW	BLUE GREEN ORANGE BLUE GREEN	YELLOW BLUE BLUE YELLOW BLUE	PINK WHITE WHITE GREEN RED
RED ORANGE GREEN BROWN PINK	GREEN BLUE YELLOW RED YELLOW	BLUE GREEN ORANGE BLUE GREEN	YELLOW BLUE BLUE YELLOW BLUE	PINK WHITE WHITE GREEN RED

Figure 2 Cards used to test reaction time.

activity Mixed messages

This activity will enable you to examine how the brain copes with mixed messages. You should complete this activity with a partner. Both of you will receive two cards similar to those shown in Figure 2.

1 Your partner should control the timer. When your partner says 'Go' you should begin reading the names of the words shown on one card. Speak clearly and say 'Stop' when you have read the last word on the card. Your partner should stop the timer and record how many seconds have passed.

2 Repeat Step 1 four more times using the same card. Compare your results to investigate if your time became shorter as you repeated the activity.

3 Now repeat Steps 1 and 2 using the second card. This time, however, you must state the <u>colour</u> of the words rather than reading what the words say. If you make a mistake, you must keep repeating the word until you get the correct answer.

4 Swap places and record the times for your partner for Steps 1 to 3.

1 **State the two main types of memory. What is the main difference between them?**

2 **Explain the difference between 'episodic' and 'semantic' memory.**

You may have had difficulty with the second activity. This is because when your eyes look at the letters of the alphabet, your brain recognises the letters. You know that normally the meaning of words is more important than their colour. This makes the task difficult because you automatically process the meaning of the word first. The brain must ignore this automatic reaction and identify the colour of the word instead, which is not an automatic process. Two reasons have been proposed to explain the effect. Speed processing theory suggests that the words are read more quickly than the colours are named. Selective attention theory suggests that more attention is needed to name the colour than read the words.

→ 9.5 How can I improve my memory?

➡️ **In this unit we are learning:**

■ techniques that can be used to improve memory (personal understanding).

How can you improve your memory?

Our brains recognise different parts of our environment such as: images, colours, structures, sounds, smells, tastes, touch, positions, emotions and language. The ability to recall information is thought to depend on how important the information is to you. It is thought to be helpful if the information helps you to create a picture in your mind. Try the activity below to find out whether this claim is true.

investigation No sense or nonsense?

Regular words: cat, moon, dog, schoolbag, ball, fire, water, coins, chair, telescope, cup, table, sofa, car, microscope.

Abstract words: happiness, anger, fear, hatred, jealous, eating, jumping, Easter, greedy, mood, true, manners, idea, Christmas, hope.

Nonsense words: jasmas, repit, racc, jensma, faterm, felty, profkl, nepwut, gilemo, wetjr, unsce, paswn, opilt, quenti, steu.

Figure 1

1 Three lists of words are shown in Figure I. Read the list of regular words twice. Cover the words and write down as many as you can remember.

2 Repeat Step I for the other two lists.

3 Compare how many words you have remembered from each of the three lists. Is there one list you could remember better than the others? Write a sentence to describe your findings.

4 Do you think your results would convince your teacher that the claim about remembering information is true? Explain your answer. What other information might you need to make your results stronger?

Linking it all together

It is easy to recall and recognise connected information that has been stored in your memory. However, it is more difficult to commit random pieces of information to memory. This means that if you can create links between the pieces of information, you will remember them more easily.

Imagine you are told the Spanish room is room 13. This fact will enter your short term memory, but unless it is important to you it is quickly forgotten. If, however, you connect the facts that the number 13 is often an unlucky number, and you are also unlucky to be studying Spanish, then you will be more likely to remember where to find the

Spanish room! There are a number of 'memory methods' that can be used to improve your memory by strengthening neuron connections across your brain.

Using mnemonics to improve your memory

Sometimes memory methods are used to link unconnected pieces of information. This is why spray diagrams are thought to be a useful way to help you remember and record information. Using mnemonics is another method used to link pieces of information together. They are easy to create, particularly if they are presented in a way that matches your preferred learning style, which you identified in Year 8. You learned then that people who use mainly visual learning think in images when they are learning. Those preferring auditory learning use sounds, and people who prefer kinaesthetic learning use more active methods.

Many people, for example, remember the colours of the rainbow, using the **mnemonic**: **R**ichard **O**f **Y**ork **G**ave **B**attle **I**n **V**ain. Here the first letter of each word in the phrase represents a different colour, which is useful for visual learners. Auditory learners might create a tuneful rhyme to help them remember the order of each colour. Kinesthetic learners could associate each colour with a different feeling such as red for anger, etc.

The mnemonic above presents a strong image. Mnemonics that use pleasant images or which are associated with pleasure are usually easier to remember. You also learned, in Unit 9.4, that brain function improves when the whole of the brain is used. This means it is important to use many types of brain function and to connect the two hemispheres of the brain.

For example you might imagine that each piece of information that you need to remember is placed in different parts of your route to school. Then as you take an imaginary walk to school you recall the information again, and in the correct sequence. You may even have used this method unconsciously if you have lost something and, in your mind, re-traced your steps to find it again. The best mnemonics are likely to include rhymes, acronyms (the first letters of the words you need to remember spell a word), or visual images.

In the following activities you will try to create some mnemonics of your own, using the link method and story method. Using these methods, you will try to link the items you have to remember with something that you are familiar with. It may help if you then try to link these together. These further links are called telling a story.

Figure 2 <u>R</u>ichard <u>O</u>f <u>Y</u>ork <u>G</u>ave <u>B</u>attle <u>I</u>n <u>V</u>ain.

Figure 3 Colours of the rainbow – Red, Orange, Yellow, Green, Blue, Indigo, Violet.

activity Making the link

1 You are given the following list of messages to pick up for your mother: coffee, butter, chips, tea and mince. An example of using the link method is:

Coffee is the drink you often have when you are eating chips. This is your favourite food and you are sitting in the sunshine – the colour of the Sun reminds you of butter. You are eating this at 5 pm. This is your teatime. For pudding you decide to have a bar of chocolate flake. This crumbles and reminds you of mince.

2 Create a link method of your own for the list above.

3 Work with a partner and, together, agree a list of five to six words. Each of you should use the link method to remember these. Swap your links with your partner to find out if your ideas match.

The story method

The following list of words: dog, park, zoo, monkey, child, sweets, money, could be used to create a mnemonic in the form of a story.

Polly has a dog, and took him for a walk in the park. On the way to the park she passed the zoo where she spied a monkey in a tree. Suddenly the monkey escaped and ran over to a small child. It grabbed the sweets from the child who screamed. A man saved the child. The child's mother was so grateful that she gave him some money.

If you prefer, the words could be organised into groups, for example organisms: child, dog and monkey; places: park and zoo; food: sweets that are bought with money.

activity Tell me a story

In this activity you will use these methods to help you develop your skills in creating mnemonics.

1 Use the link method to create a mnemonic for the following list of words: horse, dog, ball, ice cream, pen, shoe, hat.

2 Now use the story method to create a mnemonic for the same list of words. Make this a poem if you can.

3 Compare your mnemonics with some of your classmates. Do you think you would be able to use their examples?

4 Ask a partner to give you a list of 15 sports to remember. Study the list for five minutes, then cover the list and recall as many as you can.

5 Repeat Step 4 but this time, use the story method. Did this memory technique help you to remember more sports?

extension activity

Enhancing memory

Use books and the internet to find out more methods to improve memory such as converting information in words into diagram form, creating acrostics, chunking and journey methods. Try to find out more about association, imagination and location that are important for developing mnemonics.

In decline?

Did you know that your memory becomes poorer as you age? This is why you may hear older people having trouble with remembering simple facts such as a telephone number. The hippocampus is at risk of becoming weaker with age. The number of neurons in the brain, and the blood flow to the brain, can also become poorer with age. However, older people generally have no problem with remembering factual information, and their procedural memory remains fine. It just takes them a little longer to a recall long-term memories. However, there are a number of ways that you can slow this process. These include: taking regular exercise, managing stress, maintaining good sleeping habits, not smoking, and eating foods that are rich sources of the B-vitamins, omega-3 fatty acids and antioxidants.

1 Explain the term 'mnemonic'.
2 a List some of the features that are used in creating mnemonics.
  b Suggest why it is better to create mnemonics that use both hemispheres of the brain.
3 Create a list of activities that are thought to slow the ageing of the brain.

Microbes and disease

→ 10.1 Microbes

→ **In this unit we are learning:**

- details about the three main groups of microbes
- to organise information
- to reach conclusions and make logical decisions.

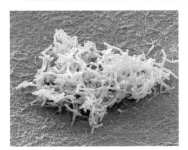

Figure 1 a *Bacillus subtilis.*

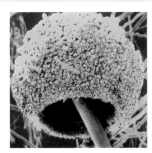

b Fruiting body of bread mould.

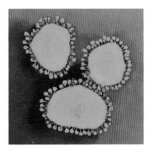

c Coronavirus particles.

What is a microbe?

Microbes are tiny organisms or micro-organisms that are generally too small to be seen with the naked eye. They are all around you, in the air and the soil. They even exist on and within your body. Fossil records show that microbes have been in existence much longer than human beings, even longer than the dinosaurs.

Microbes exist in four groups: **viruses**, **bacteria** (singular: bacterium), **fungi** (singular: fungus) and protozoa. Protozoa include a large range of organisms, like amoebae, mostly living in or near water. They will not be examined in this book, but if you want more information key 'protozoa' into a search engine.

The three main groups of microbes we consider: bacteria, viruses and fungi, vary greatly in size and shape. Bacteria have different structures as shown in Figure 2.

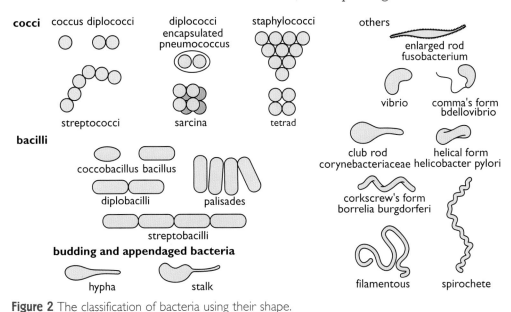

Figure 2 The classification of bacteria using their shape.

Look back to Unit 3.4 to see how bacteria help to recycle nutrients for plant growth.

Microbes have many useful roles including the digestion of litter and the production of yoghurt. Some microbes, however, can cause disease: these are called **pathogens**.

Bacteria

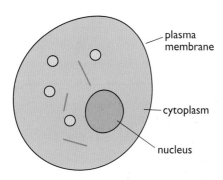

There are billions of bacteria (singular: bacterium), and they are likely to be the most numerous organisms on Earth. They are simple, single-celled organisms. Most bacteria are not harmful to human health and have important roles to play in human life including the decay of plants and animals, to recycle nutrients for plant growth. Despite their usefulness to industry, pathogenic bacteria cause food poisoning, botulism and many other diseases.

Studying bacteria

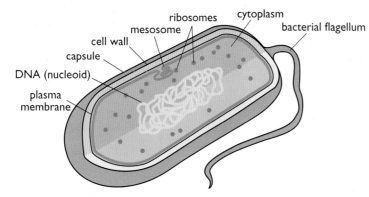

Figure 3 An animal cell (top) and a bacterium (bottom).

Although they are cells, the structure of a typical bacterium is different from that of a typical animal cell, as you can see when you compare the two diagrams in Figure 3. Bacteria exist in various shapes including spheres (*coccus* bacteria), rod shaped (*bacillus* bacteria) or in spirals (*spirillum* bacteria). *Coccus* bacteria can exist together in different arrangements including in pairs (*diplococcus*), in clusters (*staphlococcus*) or in chains (*streptococcus*).

---

activity Animal cells and bacteria

Use activity sheet *X6 Thinking Skills: Compare and contrast* to examine the differences between the bacterium and animal cell shown in Figure 3.

---

activity Shapely bacteria

1 Six pictures of bacteria are shown in Figure 4. Use Figure 2 to help you to identify the types of bacteria: *coccus*, *bacillus* or *spirillum* shown in each picture. Give reasons for your decisions. For *coccus* bacteria, identify whether the groupings are *diplococcus*, *streptococcus* or *staphylococcus*. Record your answers in your notebook.

2 If you have time, search the internet or other sources of information to find out whether each type of bacteria causes disease, and the diseases caused in humans.

Escherichia coli

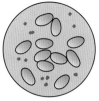
Pneumococcus

Spirillum minus

Pseudomonas aeruginosa

Pyogenes

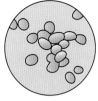
Enterococcus faecalis

Figure 4 Six types of bacteria.

Viruses

You studied viruses briefly in *Science Pathways Y8*, Chapter 3. You learned that some people have questioned whether or not viruses are truly alive, since they are not cells and do not show the seven characteristics of life. Viruses are minute micro-organisms that use the cells of other organisms to reproduce. They do not cause decay, but many are pathogens because of their ability to take over and destroy the cells of other organisms. They use these cells to produce new virus particles. This makes it more difficult to target viruses because they can 'hide' inside the cells of the body. This means they are not attacked by the white blood cells, and antibiotics are useless for destroying them.

Fungi

Fungi (singular: fungus) are classified as micro-organisms even though some, such as mushrooms and toadstools, are large enough to be seen with the naked eye. Fungi can exist as individual cells, yeasts for example, or the cells may be joined together to create long tubes called hyphae. Fungi can cause the decay of dead material and recycle essential nutrients for plant growth. Pathogenic fungi generally cause infections on the surface of the skin, such as athlete's foot that you may have seen growing between your toes!

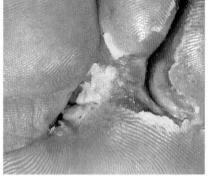
Figure 5 Infection between the toes caused by athlete's foot fungus.

---

activity Microbe mania

1 Summarise the information presented above about the three groups of microbes. You could use a spray diagram, a table, bullet points or any other way that best helps you to learn.

2 Working in a group of about three, select one group of microbes. Prepare a presentation for the members of your class to give them more information about your chosen microbe group. You could search for this information on the internet and in books. Here are some points to consider.
  – What type of organisms does this group include?
  – Are the members of the group similar in structure?
  – What conditions are necessary for the group to survive and grow?
  – Are these microbes useful to humans? If so, why are they useful?
  – Do these microbes cause disease? What types of disease do they cause?
  – Did any scientific discoveries result from studying this group of microbes? Name the scientists involved.

activity   Microbes: friends or foes?

When we hear the word 'microbe' many people immediately think of disease causing organisms. Niamh and Peter are discussing this topic with their friends George and Sally.

Figure 6

> It's not possible that microbes create medicines. We all know they cause disease.

> Microbes are germs - this means they cause disease.

> Microbes are vital for humans to live. They are used to make bread, yoghurt, cheese and even medicine.

> Microbes are useful to humans? Not likely! Microbes can cause food spoilage and even cause food poisoning!

1   Do you agree with the opinions of any or all pupils? Explain why you agree or disagree with each pupil.
2   Search the internet or books to create a list of five microbes that are useful to humans. Explain how each microbe is beneficial to humans.
3   List five microbes that cause disease and describe how they do so. List the symptoms of each disease that you have named.
4   What is your opinion? Do you consider microbes as friends or foes? Explain your answer.

extension activity   Microbe pioneers

The pioneering work of scientists has led to the discovery of the role of microbes in the spread of infectious disease. Choose one of the following scientists: Louis Pasteur, Robert Koch, Edward Jenner or Alexander Fleming. Imagine you have been sent to interview the scientist you have chosen. Make a list of questions that you would like to ask him about his work.

1 **Explain the term 'pathogen'.**
2 **Name the four groups of microbes.**
3 **When cells are invaded by viruses they are sometimes described as 'virus factories'. Can you suggest a reason for this description?**
4 **What groups of microbes cause decay?**

→ 10.2 Microbes at work

→ **In this unit we are learning:**

■ about the work of microbiologists (employability)
■ the safe practices necessary when handling microbes (personal health)
■ to assess the reliability of information about probiotics (media awareness).

Figure 1 A microbiologist at work in the cosmetics industry.

Studying microbes

Scientists who study microbes are called microbiologists. Microbiologists work in many areas of industry including the food industry, agriculture, medicine and with environmental and government agencies.

The subject of microbiology is so complex that it is divided into specific topics including medical microbiology, bacteriology, virology, etc. Many microbiologists concentrate on only one area, for example, bacteriologists study bacteria, virologists study viruses. However, all microbiologists are aware that extra safety rules are important when they are working with microbes. All microbes must be treated as potential pathogens.

activity   ## Microbe safety

This activity will teach about the safe practices that are necessary when working with microbes. The passage below gives details of some of the features of microbes and what they need to grow. There are clues for the safety precautions used when culturing microbes.

Look back to Unit 4.3 on risk assessment.

Microbes are living organisms and require a source of nutrients to live and grow. Microbes exist in a range of temperatures including some that survive in hot springs (above 100 °C). Most microbes cannot, however, survive the temperature of the flame of a Bunsen burner, which is useful for sterilising equipment. However, since microbes thrive at human body temperature, which is about 37 °C, this can lead to the spread of an infection. Many microbes also live at room temperature, where they spread unseen over all types of surface.

Clothing offers some protection from them since clothes can be removed and sterilised. This protection includes wearing a lab coat, gloves and even a mask and goggles. In addition, the human skin itself is a barrier to the entry of microbes into the body and the bloodstream. Also, the use of disinfectant soap and water offer some protection.

It is best to culture microbes in a sealed environment, so all Petri dishes should be sealed to avoid bacteria spreading through the air. Culture plates should be placed upside down and always labelled to show exactly what they contain. Plates must NEVER be opened when they are being examined. To protect everyone they should be autoclaved (heated to extreme temperatures) before they are discarded.

Figure 2 What possible sources of contamination can you see?

1 Re-read the text above and study Figure 2 carefully. Create a list of safe working practices for handling microbes. Explain why you have listed each safety practice. Create a list of unsafe working practices for handling microbes that you can spot in the picture.

2 Design an A4 poster for the kitchen of a café to alert cooks to the possible sources of microbes in their workplace.

extension activity Working microbiologists

Search books or the internet to find out the activities carried out by microbiologists working in each of the following areas: medical microbiology, food technology, agriculture. Write a summary of your findings on one of these.

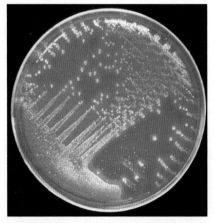

Figure 3 Cultured colonies of *Streptococcus* bacteria.

Culturing microbes

Most areas of microbiology involve growing or culturing microbes on a jelly-like substance called nutrient agar. Bacteria are generally too small to be visible to the naked eye. However, when they have multiplied in number they are easier to spot when they have grown together in groups called colonies.

investigation

Investigating the microbes in milk

In this activity you will examine the growth of microbes. Your task is to investigate whether there are microbes present in samples of milk. It is important that you use the special safety procedures for dealing with microbes that you learned about earlier.

1 Work in a group of about four people. Each group is given two agar plates. Using a permanent marker, draw a line on the base of each plate to divide it in half. Write the following words on the four areas of the two plates: (1) UHT, (2) pasteurised, (3) sterilised, (4) no milk.

2 Your teacher will show you how to correctly apply a sample of milk to each of three areas. The fourth is left untouched.

3 Seal the plates with sellotape and place them into an incubator at 30 °C.

4 To extend its shelf-life, various methods such as pasteurisation, Ultra-Heat Treatment (UHT) and sterilisation are used to treat milk. Would you expect to find microbes growing on any section of the plates? Explain your answer.

5 After 24 hours remove the plates from the incubator and examine them carefully. Make sketches in your workbook showing the four areas of the plates to create a permanent record of any microbial growth.

6 Compare the growth of microbes on the four areas of the plates. Make a statement about which type of milk enabled most microbial growth. Explain why one of the plates was left untouched.

7 Was there a difference in the amount of agar that remained on any areas of the plates? Suggest why you might find a decrease in the amount of agar where microbes have grown.

8 Find out more about the processes of pasteurisation, sterilisation and UHT that are used in the treatment of milk. After reading about these processes, were you surprised by the results of the experiment? Explain which results you did not expect to find. If you identified the growth of any microbes, suggest reasons why microbes have grown. Did the results from the class agree with your results?

9 Explain why you must not undo the sellotape, or open the plates when the experiment is completed. State how to dispose of the agar plates now that you have finished using them.

10 Suggest reasons for the following.
   a Milk is normally stored in a fridge.
   b Milk continues to turn sour even when stored in a fridge.

11 Find out the origins of the term 'pasteurisation'.

extension activity

Milk fat and microbes

Write a paragraph to explain how you would investigate whether the amount of fat that milk contains affects the growth of microbes.

Figure 4 These products are probiotics.

The friendly bacteria in dairy products

The microbes that cause milk to become sour are harmful to human health. You are unlikely to deliberately drink a liquid that you know contains microbes – or would you? Many people today consume drinks called 'probiotics', which are claimed to contain microbes such as *lactobacillus* and *bifidobacterium*. These bacteria are commonly found in the human gut. They are thought to maintain a healthy digestive system by aiding the digestion of some substances, and to produce important nutrients such as vitamin K, which helps to prevent internal bleeding. A wide range of probiotic products is available.

YAKULT
Price: £2.69 for
7 × 65ml bottle

What is it?
A fermented skimmed milk drink.

Health claims
To help 'maintain the natural balance of your digestive system' and 'benefit wellbeing.' 'A healthy way of topping up your intestine with friendly bacteria'.

Bacteria
6.5 million bacteria per dose; these are *Lactobacillus casei Shirota*

Other ingredients
10 calories,
less than 0.1g fat, 12g carbohydrate

ACTIMEL
Price: £2.38 for
8 × 100g bottle

What is it?
Probiotic yoghurt drink with *L casei imunitass*.

Health claims
To support the natural defenses of your body. To combat the imbalance caused by diet and a busy lifestyle. 'Feel the difference in a fortnight'.

Bacteria
10 billion *L casei imunitass* bacteria per dose.

Other ingredients
83 calories,
1.6g fat ,
14.3g carbohydrate

MULLER VITALITY
Price: £1.48 for
6 × 100g bottle

What is it?
A low-fat probiotic fruit flavoured yoghurt drink.

Health claims
By providing two probiotic bacteria it is more effective and can maintain the balance of bacteria in your digestive system.

Bacteria
10 billion bacteria, of two strains, *LA-5 Lactobacillus acidophilus* and *Bb-12 Bifidobacterium*

Other ingredients
74 calories, 1.4g fat, 12.8g carbohydrate, Vitamins E, B1, B2, B6.

FLORA PRO-ACTIV
Price: £2.49 for
4 × 100g bottle

What is it?
Probiotic Original Yoghurt Drink with plant sterols.

Health claims
Helps to maintain a healthy heart by including sterols that lower 'bad' LDL cholesterol.

Bacteria
About a billion *Bifidobacterium Lactis Bb-12*

Other ingredients
2g of plant sterols; 87 calories, 2.9g fat, 12.5g carbohydrate.

Figure 5 Labels from probiotic drinks.

investigation

Probiotics galore!

In this activity you will investigate four popular brands of probiotic drinks. Information about these drinks is shown on their labels (see Figure 5). Work in a group of about four people, and study the labels carefully to answer the following questions.

1 Which drink provides best value for money? Work out the price of each product per bottle, and per 100 g (or per 100 ml).
2 List the bacteria present in each drink. Do any of the drinks contain the same type of bacteria? Do any of the drinks contain the bacteria that are naturally present in the human gut?
3 Find out more information about *lactobacillus* and *bifidobacterium*. What health benefits are they claimed to have?

4 Make a list of the other ingredients in the drinks. Suggest reasons why people might be interested in the other ingredients that the drinks contain.

5 Your group may be permitted to choose one of the four types of drink. Discuss each of the drinks in turn. Provide reasons for and against choosing each drink. Your group must choose which of the four drinks you consider to be the best. Give reasons for your decision, such as the best price, etc.

6 Would the appearance of the product affect your choice of drink? Explain your answer. Would a picture help you to reach a decision over which product to choose?

7 Design a caption for a probiotic drink that would capture the attention of the general public.

extension activity   Probiotics in the media

Several reports on the topic of probiotic drinks and their benefits for human health have been reported by the media. Other articles present the view that manufacturers have made false claims about the health benefits of their probiotic products. Select one recent media article which presents either opinion and decide whether or not you agree with the view presented. Find out the reason why some manufacturers of probiotic drinks have been accused of making false claims about their products. Find out when the use of probiotics to improve health was first pioneered. Some drinks are described as 'prebiotic'. Explain the meaning of this term.

1 **Surgeons who perform operations use equipment that has been sterilised before use. Suggest why this procedure is necessary.**

2 **In the event of an outbreak of an infection in a hospital, visitors are sometimes required to put on a gown and mask. Why do you think this practice is necessary?**

3 **Manufactured foods are required to display a 'use by' date. What do you think this means? Suggest why this date is important.**

→ 10.3 Problem microbes?

→ **In this unit we are learning:**

■ to investigate the growth of fungi.

Figure 1 This bread has been allowed to decay.

Microbes and decay

You have learned that microbes can cause food spoilage. How does food decay? You may have guessed: decay is caused by the growth of microbes. Some microbes produce nasty smells, others harmful toxins or poisons. Manufacturers have developed methods to prevent the rotting of food. These methods are usually successful because they remove one of the factors microbes require for growth. You have already learned that groups of microbes cause decay, these are bacteria and fungi. Just as for most organisms, certain conditions must be present before they will begin to grow, such as moisture, air and food.

extension activity Preserving food

Find out how various methods of preservation protect food from damage by microbes. Allocate one of the following to each member of your group: freezing, salting, canning, pickling.

Figure 2 These products have been preserved using different methods. How many can you find?

investigation Requirements for growth of a fungus

In this activity you will investigate the conditions that fungi need to grow. This activity should take 12–14 days to complete.

1 Work together in groups of about four. Label four food Petri dishes (these are small containers that are used by scientists to culture/grow microbes) as follows: (1) bread and water, (2) bread and lemon juice, (3) bread and sugar solution, (4) bread only.
2 Cut a slice of white bread into quarters. Use a dropper to add 5 drops of lemon juice to one quarter piece of bread.
3 Repeat Step 2 for the sugar solution and for water.
4 Place each quarter of bread into the correctly labelled Petri dish. Place a quarter piece of dry bread in the fourth Petri dish.

Be safe: You must not eat any of the samples. Do not open the sealed plates at any time during or after the activity

Figure 3 Mouldy bread does not make a good sandwich!

5 Seal all Petri dishes securely using sellotape, and place them in a dark, warm place (at 30 °C) for seven days.

6 Figure 1 shows the appearance of a fungus on bread. Examine the bread daily for seven days and look for signs of the growth of this, or similar fungi. Each day estimate the percentage covered by fungi on each piece of bread. Record your results and plot the values on a bar chart. Was the amount of fungal growth the same on each piece? Describe the conditions that enable the fungi to grow best.

7 Find out more about the conditions fungi require for growth. Use this information to explain your results.

8 Would you have expected different results if you had placed the Petri dishes in a fridge? Explain your answer.

9 Salting is a common method of food preservation. Predict the results you would expect if you replaced the sugar solution with a salt solution. Explain your answer.

10 Suggest how you could investigate whether the type of bread is important for the results of the experiment.

---

extension activity Biodegradable materials

Microbes that make food decay are a nuisance. Have you ever considered what might happen if decay did not occur? Materials that decay are called **biodegradable.** Plan an experiment to investigate whether the following materials will decay: apple, wood, cloth, metal, plastic.

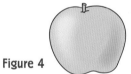

Figure 4

Look back to Unit 4.4 to see the equation for respiration.

Figure 5 Bushmills Distillery.

Fungi cause materials to decay. However, fungi are also very useful to humans. The mushrooms that you may eat for your tea are a type of fungus. Fungi are also used by the baking and brewing industries. The baking industry uses yeast to make bread and, as they grow, the fungi make bubbles of carbon dioxide gas. It is these bubbles that create the air holes in a loaf of bread. Brewers make alcoholic drinks such as beer and wine, and spirits such as whiskey. Whiskey is distilled by Bushmills Distillery in County Antrim. Fungi produce alcohol when they carry out the chemical reaction of **respiration** without any oxygen gas. This is called **fermentation**.

1 **Explain what 'fermentation' is and how it is useful to humans.**

2 **Do you think that fungi are useful or are they a problem for humans? Give reasons for your answer.**

→ 10.4 Defence against disease

→ **In this unit we are learning:**

- about defence systems in the body
- about the necessity for washing your hands (personal health).

The immune system

Every day you come into contact with people, objects and animals that are potential sources of pathogens, yet you are not continuously ill. Why? Your general health is important in the fight against infections. When you are in a state of general good health your body can combat the pathogens before they cause you any harm.

The **immune system** functions to detect and remove any foreign material that enters your body. To gain access to your body microbes must overcome various barriers. The natural ways that your body protects you from harm are shown in Figure 1. You will learn more about the role of your skin in protecting you from disease in Chapter 12.

Look back to Unit 7.4 to see the components of blood.

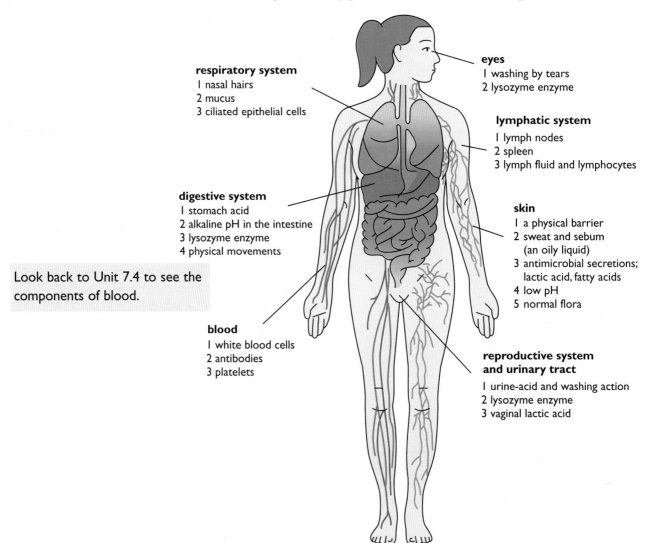

respiratory system
1 nasal hairs
2 mucus
3 ciliated epithelial cells

eyes
1 washing by tears
2 lysozyme enzyme

lymphatic system
1 lymph nodes
2 spleen
3 lymph fluid and lymphocytes

digestive system
1 stomach acid
2 alkaline pH in the intestine
3 lysozyme enzyme
4 physical movements

skin
1 a physical barrier
2 sweat and sebum (an oily liquid)
3 antimicrobial secretions; lactic acid, fatty acids
4 low pH
5 normal flora

blood
1 white blood cells
2 antibodies
3 platelets

reproductive system and urinary tract
1 urine-acid and washing action
2 lysozyme enzyme
3 vaginal lactic acid

Figure 1 The natural ways that your body protects you from harm.

activity Recording information about the immune system

To gain access to your body, microbes must overcome various barriers. This activity asks you to examine your defence mechanisms more closely.

tears

ciliated epithelial cells

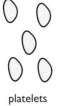

stomach acid

skin

platelets

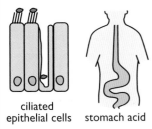

white blood cells

mucus and nose hair

Figure 2 Structures in the immune system.

1 Select three (or more) areas of the body that are shown in Figure 1. Search books or the internet to record more detail about the ability of the natural defence systems of your body to prevent infection. Explain how each of the features listed on the diagram helps to prevent microbes from causing an infection. You must decide how much information to record. Choose whatever method you prefer to record this information such as a map diagram, table format, or short bullet points.

2 Create a table to match up the structures of the body shown in Figure 2 with the description of the role they perform in the body. Choose from:
    a this traps dirt in the air
    b this kills germs in the stomach
    c this is a waterproof covering for the body
    d this is released from the nose to trap germs
    e these keep the blood clean
    f these line the respiratory system
    g this keeps the eyes free from germs
    h these create a blood clot if you cut yourself.

How do microbes gain entry to your body?

Figure 3 Wash your hands regularly.

If we know the route of entry, then we can try to prevent microbes gaining entry to our bodies. Microbes are spread by various methods including through the air, by coming into direct skin-to-skin contact with an infected person, through sexual contact, etc. You can lessen the burden on your immune system by trying to prevent the entry of microbes. One of the best methods of protection is by washing your hands regularly, particularly before you eat.

activity How clean are your hands?

With a partner, carry out this activity to find out whether you are likely to spread infections because you do not clean your hands properly.

Be safe: Take care when guiding your blind folded partner round the room

1 Your teacher will give you a dish of a thick, water soluble coloured paint. Place your left hand into the paint and ensure the underside (your palm) is completely covered with paint.
2 Your partner will tie a blindfold around your eyes. Make sure that you cannot see through the fabric. You will be taken to the sink where you should wash your hands. Try to forget that your left hand is covered with paint. Keep your hands under the tap only for the length of time that you would normally spend washing your hands.
3 When you have finished, shake off the excess water and immediately place your left hand flat on a piece of white paper. Remove the blindfold and examine the paper.
4 What do your results show about your ability to clean your hands thoroughly?
5 How does being blindfolded compare with your ability to recognise the presence of microbes on your hands? Suggest a reason why you were blindfolded for this activity.

1 Define the terms 'anti-microbial', 'antiseptic', 'antibiotic' and 'disinfectant'.
2 How do antiseptics and antibiotics differ from each other?
3 Why do hospitals generally have sinks which have elbow-operated, rather than regular hand-operated taps?

Even when you clean your hands thoroughly it is difficult to remove all microbes. Unclean hands have been recognised as being important in the spread of multi-drug resistant bacteria. These bacteria are described as 'super-bugs' for example, Methicillin-resistant *Staphylococcus aureus* (MRSA). They cause bacterial infections that are resistant to antibiotics. *Clostridium difficile* is another type of bacterium that is a major cause of infection and is described as a 'superbug'. In 2004 the National Health Service began a *Clean Your Hands* campaign. As a result, hospital wards now have alcohol-based hand rubs placed near all beds for staff and visitors to wash their hands more regularly. A wide range of commercial hand-cleansing products are available, including those that contain antiseptic and anti-microbial ingredients.

investigation How clean is clean?

How effective are commercial hand-cleansing products that claim that they provide protection against germs? Plan a safe and fair test to compare the ability of a range of commercial products to destroy microbes. Work together in groups of about four people.

You can use any of the following equipment, and any other that you require: Petri dishes, Bunsen burner and heatproof mat, sellotape, eye protection, liquid soap, bar soap, marker pen. When your plans have been checked, your teacher may let you carry out the investigation. Alternatively you may be given an activity sheet to help you to understand more about hospital infections.

→ 10.5 Stealth attack

→ **In this unit we are learning:**

- that science can help to improve the standard of hygiene for people in developing countries (sustainable development)
- that school pupils can take part in collaborative projects with professional scientists (citizenship).

How do pathogenic (disease-causing) microbes get into our bodies? We have learned already that our bodies have defences against invasion by bacteria, fungi and viruses. How do these tiny organisms slip past our defences? One of the problems is that microbes are too small for us to see, so we can eat or drink them without knowing it! There are sometimes warning signs that our food is contaminated with microbes, such as a bad smell.

One of the main problems for people in developing countries is the lack of a reliable source of safe drinking water. In Year 8 we looked at international charities such as WaterAid that aim to help people from the poorest nations to have safe water and sanitation.

It is important for scientists to share up-to-date information about their areas of work, and some organisations work in collaboration to share their skills with each other. We will find out later in this unit about a collaborative project involving scientists from the University of Ulster at Jordanstown. Charities such as WaterAid help to keep our attention on the plight of people who live far away from us, but who need our help. They provide up-to-date information on the needs of various areas, which allows us to give specific help through our giving.

I What name is given to water that is safe to drink?

activity Water update

Your teacher will give you a website to use to answer the following questions.

1 What is the present number of people who do not have access to safe water?
2 How many children currently die each year as a result of diseases caused by unclean water?
3 A simple act can reduce diarrhoeal disease by 40%. What is it?
4 Respiratory infection, such as tuberculosis, is the biggest killer of children worldwide. What is the second biggest cause of death?

A United Nations report states that half the world's hospital beds are taken up by people suffering from diseases caused by unclean water. These include cholera, typhoid and dysentery, which are all caused by different types of bacteria. Protecting people from these diseases means improving their sanitation and access to clean water, which means that human waste must be disposed of safely. In the past, these diseases also affected thousands of people in the UK.

activity The greatest doctor of all time?

Find out about the work of John Snow, the doctor who identified the source of a massive cholera outbreak in London in 1854. Dr Snow plotted the positions of the homes of cholera victims on a map (see Figure 1) that also had the locations of water pumps identified. Before this work, doctors had believed that the disease was caused by 'bad air'. John Snow was the first person to show that cholera was caused by unclean water.

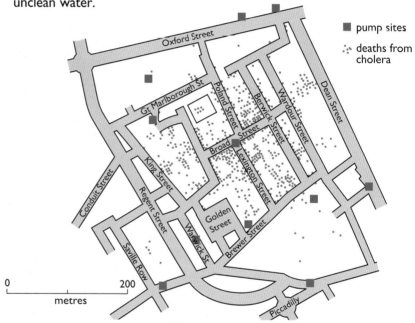

Figure 1 Map showing deaths from cholera in a small area of London in 1854.

In 2003 he was voted 'the greatest doctor of all time' by *Hospital Doctor* magazine. Do you agree? Who else might you suggest for this title?

activity Blasting bugs

Northern Ireland scientists have been involved with a new method of killing bacteria in water. Dr Tony Byrne and Dr Patrick Dunlop from the University of Ulster (UU) have helped to develop an amazing technique whereby the energy of the sun can be used to kill microorganisms. An Invest Northern Ireland report in 2007 highlighted the work of SODISWATER (solar disinfection of water), a partnership between UU and other organisations, including the Royal College of Surgeons in Ireland. You can find out more about the project at the website: **www.rcsi.ie/sodis**.

Figure 2 Glass slide with special 'photocatalysis' coating.

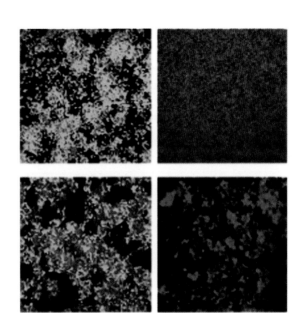

1.5 hours

3 hours

Control, TiO₂ in the dark

Control, no TiO₂ in the dark

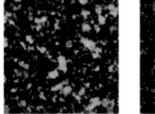 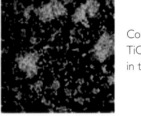

UV light only.

Photocatalysis coating in the dark (no UV) Key: green – live, red – dead.

Figure 3 Orla Clarke's investigation into *Staphylococcus epidermis* bacteria.

The UU scientists have given some Northern Ireland school pupils the opportunity to be involved in their research by offering placements for Nuffield Bursary students. While on a four-week placement, Orla Clarke carried out experiments using a special 'photocatalysis' layer developed by the UU team. She grew *Staphylococcus epidermis* bacteria on the special layer and found that by shining ultra-violet (UV) light on it, the bacteria were killed. Orla's results are shown in Figure 3. Why did Orla carry out three different tests?

---

activity **Bursary**

- If you were awarded a similar bursary, what project would you like to carry out?
- What skills and personal qualities do you have that would allow you to complete the project successfully?
- How could you promote your project in school and in your local community?

You can find out more about the Nuffield Science Bursary scheme from Sentinus: **www.sentinus.co.uk.**

→ 10.6 Microbe mania

> → **In this unit we are learning:**
>
> - to research and manage information acquired from different sources
> - to sort information into appropriate categories
> - to develop material with awareness of a specific audience.

How can we find out about microbes?

In this chapter you have learned that there are different types of microbes, including bacteria and fungi. You have also learned a little about how bacteria are classified according to their shape and associations with each other.

Look back at Unit 10.1 to help you identify bacteria.

Review your learning.

1 **What shape of bacterium is described as**
   a coccus   b bacillus   c spirillum?
2 **Pair up the following arrangements of *coccus* bacteria:**
   a *staphylococcus*   b *diplococcus*   c *streptococcus*
   with the correct description:
   i pairs   ii clusters   iii chains

Microbes are all around us, in the air we breathe, on all the surfaces we touch, in water and even on our skin. However, not all microbes are pathogens: some microbes are harmful to plants and animals, but others are very useful to humans.

Figure 1 Harmful and useful microbes.

3 **Describe two ways that microbes are harmful and two ways that they are useful. Figure 1 may help you.**

Look back at Unit 3.4 to see how bacteria are useful in decomposing dead material.

Since there are so many different microbes and also many uses for them, a lot is written about microbes. Scientists have interests in various properties of microbes, for example the ability of some microbes to produce medicine, to decompose dead material, or to make cheese and yoghurt.

Figure 2

activity Making a microbe magazine

In this activity you will work in a group to produce your own microbe magazine. The magazine should appeal to a young audience of primary school-age children. What topics might be useful to include in your microbe magazine? You will have to research appropriate information to fit in with the topic or topics you have selected, including photographs and diagrams. If you use a search engine, what key words will you use? What books or magazines can you use in the library? Are there any newspapers or magazines at home that you could obtain information from?

Think: what are the success criteria for this activity? How can you produce an attractive, easy-to-access magazine? Hints: What makes you pick up a magazine in a shop? A bright cover? A good contents list that lets you find articles easily? Interesting articles? Make a list of the points that you think are most important.

Share: As a class, decide on the success criteria each group will work with. Decide on the roles of each group member too, so that everyone can take responsibility for his own work. How will you decide on the title for your magazine?

Do: Research the information you need. Then begin to select the material you want to have in the magazine. How will you group the microbe topics? Don't forget to make a contents list for the beginning of the magazine. Put all the material you have selected into the form of a magazine and then present it to the whole class in the form of a TV advertisement.

Review: Did all groups meet the success criteria decided on at the beginning of the activity? After listening to all the presentations, evaluate the different magazines using the 'two stars and a wish' format, that is, write about two stars – two areas of each magazine that you liked – and one area that might have been improved upon.

If you decided to produce a magazine for adults your parents' age, what changes might you make to the one you used for primary school children?

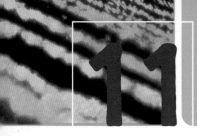
Using electricity

→ ## 11.1 What is mains electricity?

> ➜ **In this unit, we are learning:**
>
> - the difference between direct and alternating current electricity
> - how electricity is transmitted to our homes.

We use mains electricity to power different appliances such as cookers, lights and television sets, in our homes and schools. Northern Ireland Electricity (NIE) supplies us with alternating current electricity (a.c. for short) at '240 V a.c. 50 Hz'. This is the information you can see on the ratings plate on appliances in your home (see Figure 1).

Figure 1 This appliance has a rating of 2000 W at 240 V, 50 Hz a.c.

investigation Investigating d.c. and a.c.

What is the difference between d.c. (**direct current**) and a.c. (**alternating current**) electricity?

1 Set up the circuit shown in Figure 2. This circuit has direct current flowing in one direction through the bulb. The electrons always travel away from the negative terminal of the cell and towards its positive terminal.

2 Remove the cell and reconnect the circuit with the cell the other way around. The bulb still lights. This is still direct current but the electrons are travelling in the other direction.

3 Take the cell out and keep on reconnecting it, reversing the polarity of the terminals each time. Do this as quickly as you can. The bulb goes on and off repeatedly. The electrons move in one direction, then the other, and then back again. This is alternating current: it continually changes direction. However, the bulb still lights: the direction of the current doesn't matter.

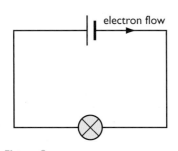

electron flow

Figure 2

The mains supply at home or school is a.c. (alternating current), as the electrons are constantly changing direction. In fact they go through a cycle of changes fifty times in one second. We say that the **frequency** of mains supply is 50 Hz. Hz is short for **hertz**, the unit of frequency, or the number of times something regular happens per second.

For most types of electrical appliances it doesn't matter whether the current is direct or alternating. A bulb will light whatever the direction of the current. If the change in a.c.

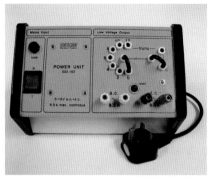

Figure 3 A power pack.

were slower we would see a flicker in the light when the electrons change direction. However, the change happens so frequently at 50 times per second that we can't see the flicker. Some appliances, like computers and televisions, need a d.c. supply, so a device called a **rectifier** is fitted inside to change a.c. to d.c.

You may have power packs in your school laboratory (see Figure 3). These take electricity from the mains at 240V a.c. but, using a transformer, supply lower voltages in the range 0 to 13V, which is safer in the laboratory. They also have a rectifier built in to convert a.c. to d.c. if this is required.

Figure 4 The power station generates electricity which is then distributed via cables on pylons.

Look back to Unit 2.2 to revise how electricity is generated.

You learned in Unit 2.2 that electricity is generated in power stations, like Ballylumford or Coolkeeragh, using turning motion between large magnets and coils of wire. If the magnets or coils turn 50 times a second, then the current reverses with the same frequency, and so we get alternating current at that frequency.

The electrical energy is then carried around the country by a grid of power cables. These lose energy to their surroundings, but there is less energy loss at high voltages, so electricity is sent through power lines at hundreds of thousands of volts. Power stations may produce voltages of 24 000V, so devices called **transformers** are used to increase or 'step-up' the voltage for transmission over long distances. Transformers are also used to decrease or 'step-down' the voltage to be used in our homes to 240V. (See Figure 4 in Unit 2.2.) Transformers work only with a.c. electricity. You'll learn about transformers in Key Stage 4 but, if you want to know how they work now, key 'transformer' into a search engine.

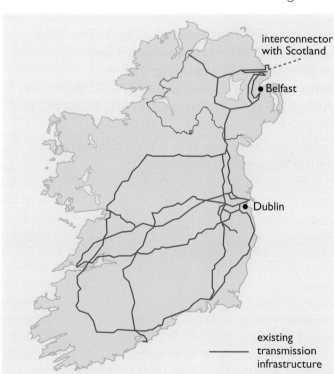

interconnector with Scotland

● Belfast

● Dublin

existing transmission infrastructure

Figure 5 The transmission network in Ireland.

Northern Ireland has its own transmission and distribution grid (see Figure 5), but it is also interconnected to Scotland and the Republic of Ireland.

Copper cables carrying electricity are buried in the ground, or light aluminium cables are suspended from pylons. Pylons can look ugly but are cheaper than underground cables. Pylons make cables easier to access for maintenance and repair.

Figure 6 a Many homes have double mains sockets like this one.

b This cell provides 1.5 V.

---

1. **Describe as fully as you can what happens to electricity from its generation to being using in our sockets.**

2. **Read through this unit and find two reasons why the mains supply a.c. electricity, not d.c. to your home.**

3. **What are the similarities and differences in the two pictures in Figure 6?**

4. **Other countries use different supply voltages. The USA mains voltage is 110 V. Give one advantage and one disadvantage of 110 V rather than our 240 V.**

5. **A mobile phone charger requires a low voltage d.c. supply. What two components must it use when it is connected to the mains supply?**

6. **Why is it a good idea that our grid is interconnected to Scotland and the Republic of Ireland?**

→ 11.2 How dangerous is electricity?

→ **In this unit, we are learning:**

■ about the hazards of mains electricity
■ to apply scientific knowledge to recognise the hazards of high voltages (personal health).

Figure 1 An electricity substation is part of the distribution network. High voltages are present and so safety warnings are displayed.

Mains electricity is about 240 volts, much higher than the voltage of a single cell. Mains electricity can send an electric shock through your body that is big enough to kill you. You get an electric shock if an electric current flows through your body to the Earth. The current can burn tissue, paralyse muscle, and make your heart quiver or stop beating.

The danger of electric shock depends more on the current that flows through your body than the voltage of the supply. This current depends on the resistance of your body. Skin resistance varies from about 1000 Ω for wet skin to about 500 000 Ω for dry skin. At large voltages the skin may be burned leaving a wound, and then there is only the resistance of the body. The internal resistance of the body is small, being between 100 and 500 Ω.

Also the amount of damage done depends on whether or not the current passes near your heart, and for how long the current passes through your body. Sometimes an electric shock can cause the victim to lose muscle control, and so not be able to escape.

Look back to Unit 6.1 to see a use of the variation of skin resistance.

1 **Why are you more likely to get an electric shock if your hands are wet?**
2 **Why is the heart so easily damaged by electric shocks?**
3 **A common saying is 'It's not voltage that kills, it's the current!' Is this true or false?**
4 **Why must we be careful at home when drilling holes in the wall doing DIY jobs?**

Every year, many people are injured or killed by mains electricity. However, some are killed by even greater voltages. At work or at play, it is vital that the dangers of coming into contact with live electricity cables are understood. The hazard sign in Figure 1 is to warn everyone about very high voltages.

activity   Dangerous activities

Figure 2 Why might these situations be dangerous?

1 Why are the people in Figure 2 in danger from electricity cables?
2 Design a publicity leaflet warning young people about the dangers of playing near electricity cables.
3 Many people are killed or injured by lightning. Find out about the causes of lightning. Is it true that 'Lightning never strikes the same place twice!'?

Figure 3

Look back to Unit 6.5 for more information on Benjamin Franklin.

Did you know?

Early scientists like the American Benjamin Franklin (1706–90) did experiments on electricity by flying kites during thunderstorms. Franklin survived, but many others were killed.

11.3 How can we use electricity safely?

In this unit, we are learning:

- how to protect against electric shock (personal health)
- to review learning using a summary map (personal understanding).

Figure 1 This kettle is connected to the mains using a three-pin plug with a fuse.

Mains electricity can kill us, so we must use it safely. Electricity must be treated with the utmost care and respect.

Electrical appliances are connected to the electricity supply by pushing a plug into a wall socket. In Britain and Ireland we normally use a three-pin plug with a fuse. The **live pin** and **neutral pins** carry the current to and from the mains supply, which is connected to the power station. The live wire is very dangerous, as it is effectively at an average voltage of 240 V with reference to the neutral wire.

Electrical appliances with metal cases must have an earth wire connected to the case. The **earth pin** in the plug is for safety: if the live wire accidentally touches the metal inside your appliance, the current is conducted to earth – not through you. The cable grip takes the strain so that if the cable is pulled the wires are not pulled out of their connections in the plug. A shutter in the socket means that the live and neutral holes in a socket are opened only when the longer earth pin is inserted.

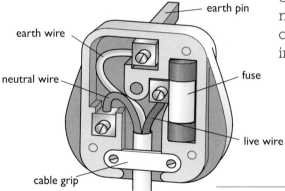

Figure 2 Connections in a three-pin plug.

1 **Copy and complete Table 1 using information from Figure 2.**
2 **Where in the plug is the fuse fitted?**
3 **Why is the cable made of copper wires covered in plastic?**
4 **Why is the earth wire striped with two colours?**

Colour of wire	Name of terminal	Function

Table 1

Figure 3 A fuse is a short thin piece of wire which melts when the current is too big.

Figure 4 A selection of fuses and fuse wire.

Confused about fuses!

Currents which are too large for an appliance can cause fires. A fuse 'blows' as a safety device to cut off the electricity when there is a fault. The fuse is always placed on the live wire. A 5A fuse will melt if a current of more than 5A flows through it. This leaves a gap in the circuit and the current does not flow. If a fuse melts it cannot be used again so it must be replaced. You should choose a fuse with rating just above the normal current so that, if the current is too high, the fuse will melt and cut off the current. Appliances with heating elements need 13A fuses, lights and TVs usually need only small fuses.

5 Give two advantages of circuit breakers over fuses.

What is a circuit breaker for?

If a current goes above a certain level the circuit breaker 'trips' off. The circuit is broken immediately and the current stops. The switch simply needs to be reset for it to work again when the fault is corrected.

Safe working with electricity is essential. All appliances should be bought with three-pin plugs correctly fitted. If a plug gets broken, it must be replaced as quickly as possible. It is vital that a plug is fitted correctly. Electrical appliances can be lethal if their plugs are not wired properly.

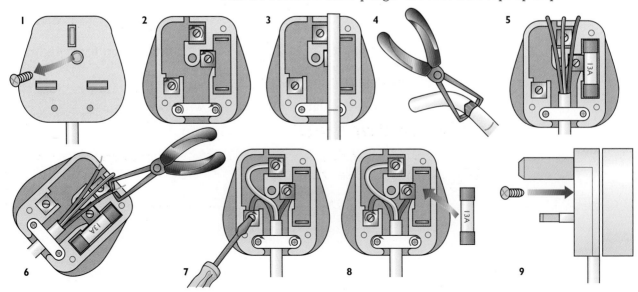

Figure 5 Steps in fitting a three-pin plug.

practical activity Wiring a three-pin plug

The sequence of pictures in Figure 5 shows the correct way to fit a three-pin plug onto the cable of an appliance.

1 Practise wiring a plug correctly.
2 Look at the pictures closely and make an instruction booklet to advise people how to safely fit a plug.

activity Fault finding

Look at the pictures of plugs in Figure 6. Discuss with a partner, in each case:

a if the plug will work
b if the plug is dangerous.

Remember: a plug can work, but can still be dangerous.

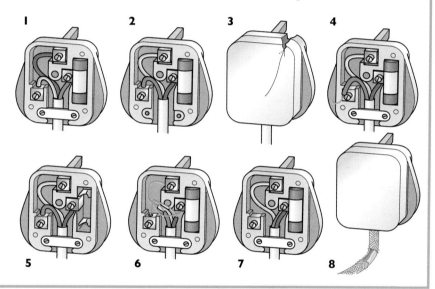

Figure 6

If an accident with electricity happens:
 – do not touch person concerned
 – if possible turn off at the socket
 – if not, push the person off the electrical source with a wooden (non-conducting) pole
 – do not use water to put out an electrical fire: use a safe foam fire extinguisher instead.

activity Electrical safety

Draw a summary diagram to link all the different measures for the safe use of electricity.

→ 11.4 How much does electrical energy cost?

→ **In this unit, we are learning:**

- to identify the power rating of an electrical appliance
- to calculate the cost of using electricity (economic awareness).

Figure 1 A 60 W filament bulb and an 11 W energy saving bulb.

Figure 2 An electricity meter.

Figure 3 An electricity bill.

You learned in Year 8 that energy is measured in units called joules. The rate energy is used at is measured in **watts** (shortened to W). One watt means one joule per second. The 60 W filament bulb in Figure 1 converts electrical energy to light and heat energy at a rate of 60 joules per second. However, most of this is lost as heat energy, rather than light. The 11 W energy saving bulb converts electrical energy to light and heat energy at 11 joules per second, but provides about as much light as the filament bulb, because less energy is lost as heat.

Electrical devices convert electrical energy into other forms of useful energy, like heat, light, sound and motion. The amount of electrical energy they convert depends on how long they are switched on for, and how fast they convert the energy.

All electrical devices have a power rating. The amount of electrical energy used is worked out by multiplying the power (in kilowatts: kW) by the time in hours. One kilowatt is one thousand watts. This amount of energy, used for an hour, is called a kilowatt-hour, which is the same as an electrical 'unit'. For example, 1 unit of electricity (or 1 kWh) is the electrical energy needed to run a 1 kW electric kettle for 1 hour, or a 100 W bulb for 10 hours, or a 2 kW fire for 30 minutes.

Using electrical energy costs money. The live and neutral electricity cables bring the supply into our homes through a meter (see Figure 2), which measures how much electrical energy is used. Electricity is measured in electrical units, and priced in pence per unit (see Figure 3). Multiplying the number of units used by the price per unit gives the cost of electricity for that period. Other costs may be added such as a standing charge for just being connected (which must be paid no matter how much electricity you use) and VAT (which is value added tax collected for the government).

1 **If 1 unit costs 11p for home customers, how much would it cost to run:**
   - **a 5 kW cooker for 30 minutes**
   - **a 2 kW tumble dryer for 1 hour**
   - **a 500 W television for 2 hours?**

2 **Arrange the appliances in Figure 4 in order of increasing power rating.**

Figure 4 Electrical appliances.

extension activity Counting the cost

An electrical 'unit' is the amount of electrical energy converted to light, heat or other forms when a 1 kW appliance is used for 1 hour. 1 kW is an energy conversion rate of 1000 joules per second.

1 At a rate of 1 kW, how many joules of energy are converted in 1 minute?

2 At a rate of 1 kW, how many joules are converted in 1 hour? How many megajoules (MJ) is this? This number of megajoules is equivalent to 1 unit of electrical energy.

3 If a unit of electrical energy costs 11p, how much is this in pence per megajoule?

4 You learned in Year 8 that we get our energy by converting food like sugar to carbon dioxide and water, with the release of energy. We can convert 1 kg of sugar to 16 MJ of energy. If 1 kg of sugar costs 96p, how much is this in pence per megajoule?

5 If you have time, try to work out how much petrol, used in a car, costs per megajoule.

→ 11.5 How is electricity used in medicine?

→ **In this unit, we are learning:**

- that nerves are electrical conductors
- how science can be used in different applications
- to identify the main points in a text (personal understanding).

Figure 1

During the 1780s, the Italian biologist Luigi Galvani discovered that the nerves in our bodies carry electrical pulses. He performed experiments on the spinal cord and legs of frogs, and watched as they twitched and jumped around. Can you explain what is happening in Figure 1? Luigi's experiments led his colleague Alessandro Volta to invent the first electric cells and batteries.

As you learned in Unit 9.1, you have nerves in every part of your body and impulses are sent electrically from your brain to all parts of your body. Information is carried around your brain by electrical connections called neurons. We feel, hear, touch, smell and think using electricity. Our heart beats because of regular jolts of electricity. We would die without electric currents in our bodies, but too much current can kill us.

Information about science can be found in many different sources. An obituary is a tribute to someone who has just died. The following text is based on a 2004 obituary for Professor Frank Pantridge, whom we met in Unit 7.5.

> Look back at Unit 6.2 for more information on electrical cells.

Professor Frank Pantridge

A Northern Ireland-born cardiologist whose pioneering techniques saved countless lives has died at the age of 88. Professor Frank Pantridge, best known for developing the portable **defibrillator**, died on Boxing Day.

Look back to Unit 7.5 to read more about defibrillators.

He invented the device in 1965 while working at the Royal Victoria Hospital in Belfast. Defibrillators provide a controlled electric shock to chests of patients to restore the heart to its normal rhythm. Mr Pantridge's invention operated from car batteries, and variants of this are now used across the world. Before this, defibrillators could only be operated from the mains electricity supply in hospitals. Dubbed 'the father of emergency medicine' Mr Pantridge installed his first portable defibrillator in an ambulance.

Around 270 000 people suffer a heart attack in the UK each year. This pre-hospital coronary care was found to reduce deaths by 38%. Cardiac arrests usually occur because of a heart attack, when the heart is starved of oxygen. The heart either quivers – known as fibrillation – or stops beating altogether. A patient's chances of survival drop by 10% for every minute that passes, meaning that having a defibrillator close at hand could make all the difference.

James Francis Pantridge (always known as Frank) was born in 1916 near Hillsborough and was educated at the local Friends' School. He graduated in Medicine from Queen's University Belfast in 1939. He immediately joined the army and made a distinguished contribution to the Second World War. He was awarded the CBE in 1978.

1 **Why is Frank Pantridge famous?**
2 **Write a summary of the science behind the story.**
3 **Choose one fact from the text which best describes something about the personal life of this famous man.**
4 **Use the internet to find out about using pacemakers in the treatment of heart conditions. What do they do? How do they work? What is their power source?**

 activity Cyborg man

Since Luigi Galvani, research into the nerves in the body has come a long way. Today, Kevin Warwick is a science professor, just like Luigi, who carries out experiments to find out more about the nerves in our bodies. He interrupts the nerves of his body and links them directly to a computer. He has also electronically linked his nervous system with that of his wife. To find out more about this fascinating scientist, and his Project Cyborg, key 'Kevin Warwick' into a search engine or go to **www.kevinwarwick.com**.

Figure 2 Kevin Warwick connected to a computer.

→ 11.6 How can I find out about local scientists?

→ **In this unit we are learning:**

- how to find out about local scientists and engineers
- to record information on local scientists
- to find out about what present day scientists do.

Figure 1 Frank Pantridge statue in Lisburn.

In Unit 11.5 you learned that Frank Pantridge from Lisburn invented a portable defibrillator, which has saved the lives of many people who have had heart attacks. Many Northern Ireland people have contributed to the development of science and engineering, including these.

- *Hans Sloane*, who was brought up in Killyleagh near Strangford Lough. His collection formed the foundation of the British Museum in London in 1759.
- *Thomas Andrews* from Comber, who designed *RMS Titanic*, and went down with the ship when it hit an iceberg in the North Atlantic in 1912.
- *John Clarke* from near Ballycastle, who developed potatoes that were resistant to the blight that destroyed potatoes which had led to the famine which killed over a million people in Ireland in the 1840s.
- *Harry Ferguson* from Dromore, who invented the Ferguson System to link tractors more efficiently to the farming equipment they pulled.
- *Jocelyn Bell* from Lurgan, who discovered neutron stars. These are collapsed remnants of dead stars, with a density of over a hundred million tonnes per cubic centimetre.

activity   Local heroes

Choose one of the scientists or engineers listed above, or another local scientist you have heard about. Key the name into a search engine to find out more about him/her. Download activity sheet *X16 Famous scientist or engineer*, and use this to record information about this scientist or engineer.

There are many scientists working in Northern Ireland today. You can find out more about these people, and what they do, on the internet.

activity   Present day scientists

Choose one of the scientists you have found on the internet. Download activity sheet *X17 Local scientist or engineer*, and use this to find out and record more about him/her.

Skin and feeling

→ **12.1 Armour plating?**

→ **In this unit we are learning:**

- how our skin can act as our first line of defence against damage and disease
- to develop our learning by connecting new information to what we already know
- to summarise information about defence against disease in the form of a poster.

practical activity Skin deep

1 Look at your skin through a lens, or a microscope if available. In your notebook, draw and describe what you see.
2 Stick a piece of sellotape to the back of your hand, then remove it so that it peels off some dead cells. Look at these under the microscope.

Look back at Unit 10.4 to read more about your body's natural defences.

How does our skin protect us?

In Chapter 10 you learned that skin is one of the body's 'natural defences'. How does skin protect us? One important way our skin helps us is that it keeps our insides in! It also forms a barrier to germs. The skin is the largest **organ** in the body. It has a total area of about 2 square metres, it has about 300 million cells, and makes up about 10% of our total body mass. It is waterproof and tough, yet it can bend and stretch.

Your skin is made up of different layers, the two main ones being the epidermis and the dermis. You will learn about the detail of these layers in Unit 12.2. New cells formed at the base of the epidermis (the 'basal layer', see Figure 1) are square-shaped cells that become flatter as they move outward, pushed up by newer cells forming underneath. The flattened cells are called 'squamous epithelium' and overlap each other to form a protective barrier.

As the cells move upwards towards the skin surface two important things happen:

1 the cells become filled with **keratin**, a tough protein that is insoluble in water
2 the cells move far away from capillaries and so are no longer nourished by the blood.

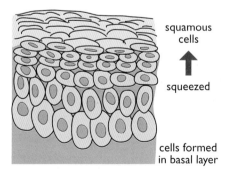

squamous cells

↑

squeezed

cells formed in basal layer

Figure 1 Skin.

By the time they reach the surface they have lost their nuclei (singular: nucleus) and are dead.

These dead cells, filled with keratin, act as a tough, waterproof barrier to germs. We constantly lose these squamous cells from our skin surface – a process called **desquamation**. The dust that floats around us at home or in school is made up mainly from dead skin cells.

Figure 2 Your skin protects you from germs.

activity Our skin as armour?

How is your skin similar to the protective armour worn by medieval knights? How is it different? You can download activity sheet *X6 Thinking skills: compare and contrast* to help you.

Our skin is the part of our body that has first contact with our surroundings. If our body were a fortress, the skin would be like the strong walls protecting everything inside. We also have a type of 'patrol' scouting the outside of the fortress, in the form of our sweat and tears! Both of these substances contain bactericides – molecules that can attack microbes.

A substance called sebum, secreted by oil glands in the dermis, helps to waterproof the skin. The skin has other functions, as well as defence, including temperature regulation, insulation, formation of vitamin D, and sensing changes in our surroundings. You will learn more about these functions in the rest of this chapter.

Figure 3 Skin is like the strong walls of a fortress.

activity Developing our learning

1 Working in pairs, use the new detail in this section, together with the information you already have from Unit 10.4 to create a poster summarising the body's natural defences.
2 Use the analogy of a fortress to represent the skin around the body. What type of defences (or defenders) might you have inside the fortress representing the acid in your stomach or the white cells in your blood? Make sure that you include explanations, describing the functions (jobs) of the different defensive features in your poster.

→ 12.2 Skin deep

→ **In this unit we are learning:**

- to identify the structure of skin
- that information can be expressed in different ways
- to work collaboratively in a group to develop knowledge.

Does skin have a structure?

The skin is an organ, which means that it is made up from different tissues. Our skin has two main layers: the surface epidermis (the outer layer) and the softer dermis (the inner layer). Underneath the dermis is a layer of fat, also known as 'subcutaneous' tissue, which helps to insulate the body. The epidermis and dermis are made up of different types of tissue.

The **epidermis** consists of several layers, the deepest of which is called the basal cell layer. This is where cells divide to produce millions of new skin cells every day and where melanin-containing cells are found (melanin helps to protect skin cells from sunlight damage).

Above the basal layer is the 'spinous cell layer' (or stratum spinosum) and then comes the 'granular cell layer' (stratum granulosum) where keratin is added to the epidermal cells. The final, outer cell layer is called the stratum corneum (or 'horny layer'), where the now dead skin cells lie in overlapping layers to form a tough, waterproof barrier.

The **dermis** lies underneath the epidermis. This is where we find blood capillaries, nerves, sweat glands, hair follicles and sebaceous glands. Directly below the basal layer of the epidermis is the papillary layer of the dermis. This ridged, bumpy layer is most easily seen in the tips of our fingers, where it forms our fingerprints. These tiny ridges provide us with the friction we need to allow us to hold on to and grip objects.

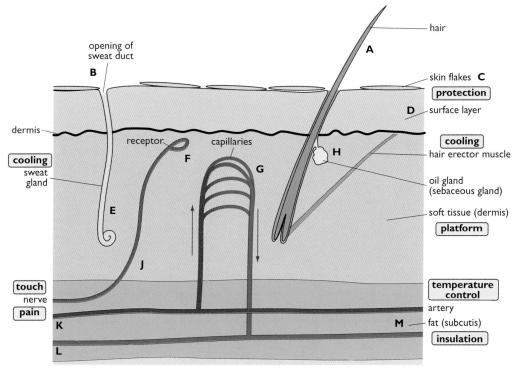

Figure 1 Skin layers.

1 **What is the name of the dead outer layer of skin?**
2 **What are the two main skin layers?**
3 **Give two similarities and two differences between these main layers of skin.**

4 **What is the name of the gland labelled (E) in Figure 1? Try to explain why it opens onto the skin surface.**

5 **Arteries carry blood away from the heart. What is the type of blood vessel labelled (L), which carries blood back to the heart?**

---

activity Skin structure

Think: Working by yourself, use the information in the text above to label structures (a) to (d) in the diagram that your teacher will give you showing the structure of skin.

Pair: Compare your diagram with that of your partner. Are your diagrams similar?

Share: Review the diagrams with your teacher and the rest of the class. Did you have difficulty deciding how to label the diagram? Was there any additional information you might have needed?

---

activity Building up knowledge: peer support

Using your labelled diagram, work in a small group to add notes explaining the *functions* of the different structures. For example, to the label 'basal cell layer' you might add 'new epidermal cells are produced here'. You can use the information in the text and any additional information you might gather from books or websites.

Now try Questions 1 to 5 again. Did you find the questions easier after labelling the diagram? Which description helped you to answer the questions best, the text or the diagram? We each learn in different ways and some people find that they can learn information more easily when it is represented in a diagram. As you saw in Unit 9.5 on improving your memory, using a diagram is a way to rehearse your knowledge and so reinforce the details in a topic, in just the same way that an actor rehearses lines by repeating them.

---

activity Reviewing learning

1 Your teacher will give you the address of a website where you can consolidate and review your learning by reading the sections on 'skin structure and function'. The different sections have self-evaluation quizzes at the end, which you should complete. By reading information from different sources you can improve your knowledge and understanding of a topic. You can use some of the new information from the website to make additional notes on your 'skin' diagram, for example, the time taken for skin cells to move from the basal layer to the skin surface.

2 When you have completed all the activities, take time to try to draw your own diagram of the structure of the skin from memory. How many structures were you able to remember?

3 Write a short paragraph (about 50 words) describing the different layers in skin.

→ 12.3 Are you feeling OK?

→ **In this unit we are learning:**

- that observing the appearance of your skin can provide information about your health (personal health)
- to use visual evidence to compare and contrast skin conditions
- to ask questions that can be investigated.

Figure 1 Skin helps to regulate body temperature.

The appearance of our skin can reflect how healthy we are. Sometimes people will ask us if we are feeling well because they have observed that our skin is pale, or perhaps flushed (looks red). If you have a higher temperature than normal, one of the first signs is that your skin becomes flushed. Why does this happen? One of the properties of skin is that it helps to regulate our body temperature.

In Unit 12.2 you learned about skin structure. Tiny capillaries lie in the dermis, close to the skin surface. If we become too hot, more blood flows through these blood vessels in order to radiate away the excess heat. Have you ever heard the expression 'blue with cold'? When the body temperature falls *below* normal, blood is directed *away* from the skin's capillaries, so the colour of the skin changes and becomes paler.

sweat gland

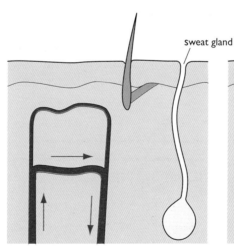

Blood is directed away from skin surface to prevent heat loss by radiation. Skin looks pale. Raised hairs trap air for insulation.

Figure 2 a Body conserving heat.

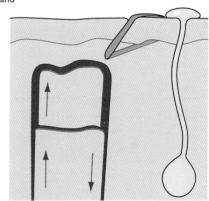

Blood flows near to skin surface to increase heat loss by radiation. Skin looks flushed. Sweat evaporates, causing cooling.

b Body radiating heat.

investigation Cool it!

Be safe: Be careful when using hot water

We can lose heat from our skin in different ways: by radiation, convection and conduction.

Which of these methods would be most effective if we are too hot? You can use temperature sensors to measure the heat loss from test tubes of hot water in different conditions.

1 Leave a test tube filled with hot water to simply radiate heat into the surroundings.
2 Place a test tube in the flow of air from a fan (this transfers heat energy by convection).
3 Put a test tube into a beaker of cold water (this transfers heat energy by conduction).

Think: In a group of about four, carry out an investigation into the most efficient method of heat loss. You will need to make some decisions before you begin, for example, what would you need to measure? What would you change/keep the same? How will you record and display the results? What other factors do you need to consider in order to have a reliable, accurate investigation?

How could you change your experiment to test the effect of different types of clothing on the rate of heat loss?

Our skin can also show symptoms of **infection**. Oil glands (sebaceous glands) are located next to hair follicles and secrete a substance called sebum. Unfortunately, if the pore becomes blocked with excess sebum, the conditions are just right for bacteria to grow, with a perfect temperature and plenty of food, resulting in acne. In *Science Pathways Y8* you learned about the link between puberty and acne, when the sebaceous glands can produce a lot of sebum.

The infection causes a spot or boil on the skin surface, which may be red and swollen due to an increased blood supply as the body sends white blood cells to fight the infection. The white blood cells combine with dead bacteria to form pus. More serious boils can result from other situations, such as an ingrown hair. Larger boils may need to be lanced by a doctor or nurse in order to drain the **pus** away.

Our skin can suffer in other ways, not caused by microbe infection. Have you ever had a blister on your foot because your shoes rubbed your skin? Blisters are different from spots because they are caused by friction, not infection.

activity Friction or infection?

1 Look at the photographs in Figure 3. Can you tell by simple observation which of the skin conditions is due to an infection? How could you make your decision? What other questions might you need to ask? What other tests might you need to carry out?

2 Use a key to help someone to identify the different conditions shown above. Keys involve asking a series of questions where there are two choices each time. Some choices may lead to further questions, others will provide the answer you seek.

3 With a partner, make a list of childhood infections that cause symptoms that can be seen on the skin. Research two of these infections and add them to the key you produced in Step 2 above.

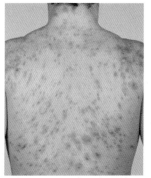

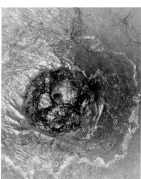
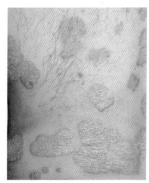
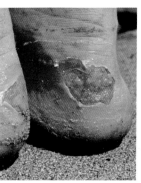

Figure 3 a Acne scarring. **b** Boil. **c** Psoriasis. **d** Blister on heel.

activity Skin activity

Components of your skin include: (1) surface (epidermis), (2) soft tissue (dermis), (3) hair and oil glands, (4) sweat glands, (5) nerves, (6) blood (in arteries, capillaries and veins), and (7) fat. These help in the following processes: (A) temperature control, (B) heat insulation, (C) energy storage, (D) sense of touch, and (E) protection from harm. You may find Figure 1 from Unit 12.2 and Figure 2 from this unit useful.

Match each process with the appropriate component(s) of your skin, by linking each letter to one or more numbers. Some components may take part in more than one process. You can find useful information about your skin on the British Association of Dermatologists' website.

→ 12.4 What happens when skin is damaged?

→ **In this unit we are learning:**

■ the importance of good hygiene in preventing infection (personal health)
■ about the dangers of damaged skin
■ to reflect on personal practice to improve health (personal health)
■ to research, collate and manage information.

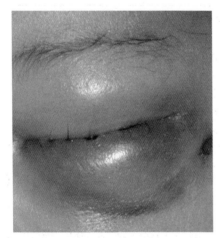

Figure 1 *Staphylococcus aureus* causes problems if it enters the body.

Skin acts as a barrier to microbes when it is intact, but what happens if we have a cut or graze? The microbes on and in our bodies enormously outnumber our own cells. Microbes like to live on our skin, but these bacteria can actually be good for us! The surface of the skin is made up from dead cells, forming a very dry layer, which most microbes do not like.

However, our skin does secrete some substances such as oils that bacteria like to feed on. The bacteria that live on the skin surface help us by preventing the growth of pathogenic (disease-causing) microbes, so in a way they act as little hordes of defenders. The negative part of this is that when our skin is damaged, these 'beneficial' bacteria can get into the living tissue underneath the dead skin surface.

Millions of bacteria live on our skin surface and are called 'commensals', which means that they do not normally cause us any ill effects. A microbe called *Staphylococcus aureus* lives on our skin, but it can cause boils and 'styes' if it gets under the skin. *Staphylococcus epidermis* also usually lives harmlessly on our skin, but it can also cause problems if it enters the body.

Our microbial invaders soon come up against the body's other defence mechanisms. Recall Unit 10.4, which describes body defences such as white blood cells. The skin begins to repair itself soon after the damage is caused. First of all the wound is 'plugged' by the formation of a blood clot, which prevents more microbes entering. This creates a 'scab', which protects the new skin forming by cell division underneath. Your teacher will give you a website where you can watch an animation of the steps in skin repair.

I Think back to Unit 10.1: *Microbes*. **Can you work out the shape of *Staphylococcus aureus* from its name?**

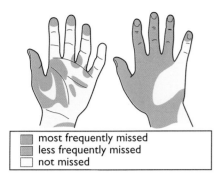

most frequently missed
less frequently missed
not missed

Figure 2 Missed spots when hand-washing.

How can we reduce the likelihood of a cut becoming infected?

We learned the importance of washing our hands in Unit 10.4, and carried out an experiment to assess the benefit of effective hand washing. Figure 2 shows the areas that we usually miss when we wash our hands. When we get a bad cut, the first thing we must do is to wash the wound and possibly apply disinfectant. Sometimes we will be advised not to touch the area. Why should we not touch cuts or grazes?

2 **Which areas are most frequently missed when we wash our hands?**
3 **Can you explain why these areas are neglected?**
4 **Look at your own hands and try to explain why bacteria might like to live in these 'missed' areas.**
5 **How can you change the way you wash your hands in order to prevent missing these areas?**

---

activity Scrub-a-dub-dub!

1 Using a search engine, research the way surgeons wash their hands before an operation. What key terms will you use for your search? Make a note of any changes you make to your list of 'key terms'.
2 Write a report to explain the differences between the way surgeons and school pupils wash their hands.
3 Finally, create a bright poster that could be put in the school washrooms to encourage good hand-washing practice. A useful website is: **www.kidshealth.org**.

Another property of our skin helps us when we get a cut or graze. The pain receptors in the dermis give us a warning that something bad has happened! If we were not aware of cuts and damage to the skin, we would not be able to take action to prevent infections.

→ 12.5 Keep your hat on!

→ **In this unit we are learning:**

- the importance of staying safe in the sun (personal health)
- about the work of the Ulster Cancer Foundation (citizenship)
- to adapt information for a different audience (media awareness).

How can we protect ourselves in the Sun?

The Ulster Cancer Foundation reports that skin **cancer** is continuing to rise in Northern Ireland, and is the most commonly diagnosed type of cancer in our Province. We can reduce our risk of getting skin cancer by not getting sunburned: all the sun exposure we get as children contributes to our likelihood of suffering from skin cancer when we are older. A useful source of information and guidance can be found on the website **careinthesun.org**.

Figure 1 When playing in the sun, make sure that your skin is well protected.

Figure 2 Different phototypes.

How does something as pleasant as sunshine increase our cancer risk? Sunlight is made up from different types of radiation, including infrared (the radiation that we feel as warmth) and UVC, UVB and UVA (types of ultraviolet light), which can cause skin damage. The skin reflects some of this radiation, but some is absorbed and can even penetrate as far as the upper dermis level. After exposure to sunlight our skin produces melanin, a dark pigment that helps to protect our cells from sun damage.

Unfortunately if we stay in the sun too long our skin starts to burn and can become so badly damaged that the upper layer actually peels away. Melanin can filter UVB and UVA radiation and so protect the skin cells, but the level of this pigment is different depending on our skin 'phototype'. Our phototype is determined by our skin's response to sunlight. Thomas Fitzpatrick, a dermatologist, first proposed the classification in 1975.

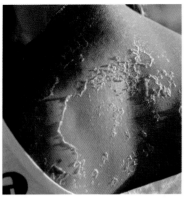

Figure 3 Over exposure to the Sun can cause skin damage.

Fair skinned people with red or blonde hair are more at risk from sunburn and so are more at risk of developing skin cancer. Children are also more at risk from sunburn than adults, as the body is slower at producing melanin in people under 15 years old. If UVB and UVA radiation penetrates to the basal layer of skin, the production of new skin cells may be altered. Cell division becomes abnormal and may lead to the development of a tumour. If the tumour develops in 'melanocytes', the cells that produce melanin, a 'melanoma' can occur.

activity Staying safe in the sun

1 Go to the Ulster Cancer Foundation website and click on the 'care in the sun' link under 'Quick links'. From here you can download the 'Ulster Fries' leaflet.
2 Read the leaflet on your own.
3 After reading the leaflet, work in a group to produce a version for primary school pupils (aged 9 to 11). What changes would you have to make to the 'Ulster Fries' leaflet to make it suitable for young children? In your version, include the tips that you consider most important for safety in the sun. You can check safe skin exposure time at **uk.weather.com**.

Note that, just like other skin cells, the ones containing additional amounts of melanin also move upwards from the basal layer through the different levels of the epidermis – this explains why we eventually lose our suntan!

activity Dress to impress

1 In a group, design an investigation into the effectiveness of different fabrics in protecting the skin from solar radiation. What types of fabric would be most suitable for very warm weather? How will you measure the intensity of radiation. Hint: check the different types of sensor available for use with the Log-It.
2 Design an outfit appropriate for a journey outdoors at the equator.

→ 12.6 Tickly feet?

Too many stimuli!

Figure 1

By simply observing our own bodies we can see that skin is not the same in every area. Our skin has a different appearance depending on where it is located on the body. Your eyelids have the thinnest skin on your body. The skin on your face is about 0.12 mm thick: the skin on the soles of your feet may be twenty times thicker. The skin can be different in other ways too, such as colour, hairiness and sensitivity.

Did you know?

On average your skin has about 60 sweat glands, 50 touch receptors, 40 sebaceous glands, eight hairs and about 700 mm of capillaries, on each square centimetre.

investigation

Be safe: Make sure that you do not press the skin too hard with the paperclip

Investigating skin sensitivity

In this activity you will work in pairs to investigate if skin sensitivity is different on different parts of the body. You should use at least three areas of skin, including the fingertips, the inside of the lower arm and the outside of the upper arm. The activity investigates our ability to distinguish a stimulus as two separate points rather than a single point, and depends on our sense of touch only. How can you make sure that you investigate touch and not sight?

Open up a paperclip and use a ruler to set the two points about 5 mm apart. Touch your partner's skin with the ends of the opened paperclip, then gradually decrease the distance until the person feels only one 'point' instead of two. Agree with your partner the method you will use for this investigation, including how you will record your observations. Show the method to your teacher before you begin.

Take turns so that both you and your partner have a chance to investigate your skin sensitivity. The smallest distance at which you can make out (or 'distinguish') two points instead of one is your own 'sensitivity threshold' for that area of skin.

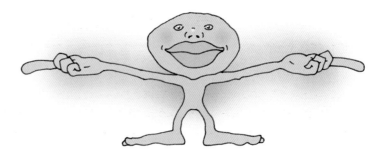

Figure 2 This cartoon shows which parts of your body have the most receptors for touch.

The skin has different types of receptor within the dermis, allowing us to determine changes in our environment: these changes are known as stimuli (singular: stimulus). Examples of stimuli include touch, pressure, pain and heat (or cold).

The density of these different types of receptors explains why our skin has areas with different sensitivity. Can you predict which parts of your body have most receptors for touch? You can find a clue at: 'your really weird body map' **faculty.washington.edu**.

As you can see from Figure 2, the most sensitive areas of your body include the lips, fingertips and feet. Perhaps this explains why some of us have tickly feet!

---

activity Why can pain be a good thing?

Consider this: You might think that pain is a bad thing, but it can be very good for you!
Can you suggest why?

Figure 3 When pain can be a good thing!

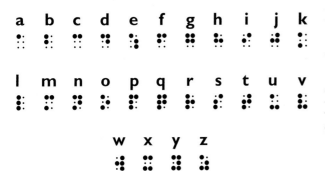

Figure 4 The Braille Alphabet.

---

1 **Which parts of your body are most sensitive to touch?**
2 **Can you predict how the volume of a Braille book would differ from the same book in ordinary typed text?**

Do you remember Figure 1 in Unit 12.2 showing the structure of your skin? In it, the dermis is shown to have folds, which can be seen best on our fingertips where they make our unique fingerprint. The folds provide a large surface area, so the fingertips have a greater density of touch receptors, or 'sensory receptors'.

People who are visually impaired can use their fingertips to 'read', by identifying the shapes of the letters as described by Braille characters.

Think back to your investigation into skin sensitivity. Scientists have found that the sensitivity threshold, allowing us to distinguish a single point, is between 1 mm and 3 mm on the fingertips. How does that compare with your own skin sensitivity? Because of this sensitivity threshold, Braille characters are 4 mm × 6 mm, which means that an A4 page of Braille has 27 lines of about 30 Braille characters. How does this compare with a page of 'normal' script?

Glossary/Index

Word / phrase	Unit	Explanation
abiotic factors	3.1, 8.1	the non-living or physical parts of an ecosystem
absorption	4.6	the process that allows the uptake of nutrients from the gut into the bloodstream
aerobic exercise	7.1	moderate physical activity that takes place when oxygen produced by respiration is available for muscles
alkali metals	1.6	a family of elements in group 1 of the Periodic Table
alternating current	11.1	electric current which constantly changes direction back and forth
alveolus/alveoli	7.3	tiny air sacs where gas exchange occurs
ammeter	6.2	a meter used to measure current through a circuit
ampere	6.2	unit of electric current
amygdala	9.1	part of the limbic system of the brain that has a role in processing and memory of emotions
analogy	6.1	a similar situation in another context used to help explain
animal cell	3.1	a cell with characteristics that show it belongs to an animal
antioxidant	9.2	molecules that prevent the addition of oxygen to other molecules by removing particles called free radicals that can damage cells
anus	4.6	the opening at the end of the gut that faeces is passed through when it is removed from the body
asteroid	3.6	a rocky object that orbits the Sun between the orbits of Mars and Jupiter
asthma	7.3	a disease of the respiratory system when the air passages become narrow, swollen and at times lined with mucus in response to one or more factors
atom	1.5	the smallest particle of an element
atomic number	1.5	the number of protons in the nucleus of an atom
atria	7.4	the two chambers present at the top of the heart that receive blood from the two main veins of the body
axon	9.1	a long nerve fibre that carries electrical impulses in the neuron
bacterium	10.1	a single cell microorganism, normally a few micrometres in length. They have a wide range of shapes, for examples, spheres, rods and spirals
balanced diet	4.1	a diet that contain all seven food groups in the correct amounts for good health
Basal Metabolic Rate (BMR)	7.1	the amount of energy used by the body when at rest in average room temperature, the amount of energy released to allow the organs of the body to function
battery	6.2	a collection of electrical cells
biochemical	3.2	a chemical that originates in a living thing
biodegradeable	10.3	a type of waste from plant or animal sources, which can be broken down by other living organisms
biomedical scientist	7.4	a scientist who increases knowledge on topics related to medicine
biotic factors	3.1, 8.1	the living parts of an ecosystem
blood donor	7.4	a person that volunteers to have blood removed from his or her body to give to another person
blood transfusion	7.4	the process when blood is removed from a blood donor and given to a recipient

Word / phrase	Unit	Explanation
bronchioles	7.3	fine tubes that do not contain cartlidge and divide from the bronchus. They are less than 1 mm in diameter and carry air to the alveoli
bronchus	7.3	one of a pair of tubes that connects the trachea to finer tubes called bronchioles
cancer	9.2, 9.3	a disease that results in the abnormal and uncontrolled division of body cells
capillary	7.3	a tiny blood vessel of the body
carbohydrates	3.1, 4.1	a large group of compounds including starch, cellulose and sugars that are used as a source of energy
carbon dioxide	7.1	a gas that is only a fraction of the air and is released by the combustion of fuels and in respiration
carbon footprint	1.2	your personal measure of how much carbon dioxide you produce
carbon-based	3.2	built or based around the element carbon
cardiac muscle	7.4	a type of muscle tissue that is present in the heart
catalyst	1.4	a substance which speeds up chemical reactions without being chemically changed
cell	6.2	(electricity) produces electrical energy from a chemical reaction
chemical formula	1.8	represents the chemical composition of a compound
chemical reaction	1.7	where new substance(s) is formed from one or more reactant(s)
chemical symbol	1.8	a unique code for an element which is recognised internationally
cholesterol	7.5	a fatty substance that is carried in plasma and increases the risk of heart disease because it can narrow arteries
circulatory system	7.5	the system that moves substances to and from cells and includes the heart, blood vessels and blood tissue
climate change	2.4	the variation in the Earth's weather systems
combustion	7.1	also called burning, this chemical reaction produces water, energy and carbon dioxide when a fuel is set alight in the presence of oxygen gas
comet	3.6	a 'dirty snowball' that orbits the Sun
community	3.1	the collection of plant and animal populations that occupy a particular habitat
competition	3.4	when individuals of the same species or different species fight for food, light, space, etc.
compound	1.7	a chemical substance made up of two or more elements joined together
conclusion	5.6	the final paragraph of a report, summarising its ideas
conductor	6.1	a material which allows electric current to flow through it
conservation of energy	2.1	a scientific law which states that the energy at the start is always the same as the energy at the end
constipation	4.6	a condition of the digestive system when hard faeces are produced that are difficult to expel from the body
coronary artery	7.5	the artery that supplies the heart muscle with blood
corpus callosum	9.1	a band of neurons that connects the two hemispheres of the brain
decomposers	3.4	organisms that break down dead material, e.g. bacteria and fungi
defibrillator	7.5, 11.5	a machine used to send an electric shock into a patient's heart to restart it
dermis	12.2	the living layer of skin underneath the epidermis
desquamation	12.1	the process by which dead epidermal cells are removed from the skin surface
development	5.6	the main element of a report or summary
digestion	4.6	the breakdown of complex nutrients from large, insoluble food molecules to small, soluble particles

Word / phrase	Unit	Explanation
direct current	11.1	electric current which always flows in one direction
distillation	1.4	a method of separating pure liquids using evaporation
DNA	1.5, 3.1	deoxyribonucleic acid – a chemical substance in living cells which carries genetic information
dry mass	3.3	the mass of a substance once all water has been removed
earth pin	11.3	the longest pin on an electric plug which is connected to the earth wire
ecosystem	3.1, 3.5	the community of living organisms and the abiotic factors they interact with
electric circuit	6.1	the path along which electric current flows
electric current	2.2	the flow of electricity in the form of charged particles
electricity	2.1, 2.2	electrical energy
electrolysis	1.7	the process of passing an electric current through a solution, causing a chemical change
electron	1.5	a subatomic particle outside the nucleus with a negative charge
electron flow	6.5	the movement of tiny negatively charged particles
element	1.1	a single substance made up of just one kind of atom
environmental variable	8.1	a factor that can change or be changed in the environment
enzyme	4.5	a protein that is a catalyst, which speeds up a chemical reaction; enzymes react with only one type of reactant and are not altered by the reaction
epidermis	12.2	the dead outer layer of skin
episodic memory	9.4	the memory of events, times and places associated with emotions
exhaled air	7.2	air that passes out of the lungs and is expelled from the body during breathing
extraterrestrial	3.6	something from outside the Earth
faeces	4.6	a waste product that is removed from the gut by the process of defecation
fat	3.1	one of the types of food necessary for a balanced diet; helps to insulate us
fats	4.1	a complex food group made from smaller units of fatty acids and glycerol; used as an energy source and for protection and insulation
fermentation	3.3, 10.3	a type of respiration without oxygen that produces alcohol, also called 'anaerobic respiration'
fibre	4.1	indigestible material made from the cell walls of plant material
food chain	3.1, 3.2	the feeding relationship between different organisms
fossil fuels	2.2	energy sources formed from the organic remains of plants and animals
fractional distillation	1.4, 5.5	a method of separating liquids with close boiling points
frequency	11.1	the number of times something regular happens every second
fungus	10.1	a plant-like organism that lacks chlorophyll
gas (gaseous) exchange	7.3	the process where oxygen and carbon dioxide gas pass across a respiratory surface such as the alveoli
glucose	3.1, 4.6	one of the simple carbohydrates used to provide energy in respiration
glycogen	3.1	a carbohydrate storage molecule found in liver and muscle cells
good health	4.1	when the health status of the body functions at an optimal level and is not suffering from the effects of illness
gravity	8.4	a force that pulls objects together
greenhouse gases	2.4	gases in our atmosphere which trap heat energy in the Earth's atmosphere
group	1.6	the vertical columns of the Periodic Table

Word / phrase	Unit	Explanation
gut	4.6	the digestive tract that includes the organs necessary for the breakdown of complex nutrients, their absorption and digestion
habitat	3.1	the place where an organism lives
halogens	1.6	a family of elements in group 7 of the Periodic Table
hazard	4.3	anything that may cause harm, such as chemicals, electricity, working insecurely
heart	7.4	an organ made from cardiac tissue that pumps blood around the body
hemisphere (brain)	9.1	one of two halves of the brain cerebrum
Hertz	11.1	the unit of frequency, the number of times a regular occurrence happens per second
hippocampus	9.1	part of the brain present in both hemispheres, is part of the limbic system and has a role in memory and spatial navigation
hypothalamus	9.1	a gland found at the top of the brain stem that regulates the body's metabolism
igneous	8.2, 8.3	a type of rock made from volcanic activity
immune system	10.4	mechanisms within an organism that protect it from disease
infection	12.3	attack by microbes
inference	3.6	hypothesis, theory or idea
inhaled air	7.2	air that travels into the lungs from the surroundings during the process of breathing
insulator	6.1	a material which does not allow electricity to flow through it
introduction	5.6	the initial paragraph of a report, setting out what will be covered in the report
joule	4.4	the unit used to measure energy
junk food	4.1	food that is thought to have poor nutritional value for the body
keratin	12.1	a structural protein that gives strength to hair and nails
kilocalorie	4.4	a unit that represents 1000 calories; it is approximately the amount of energy needed to raise the temperature of 1 kg of water by 1 degree Celsius, which is about 4.184 kilojoules
kilojoule	4.4	a unit that represents 1000 joules
landscape	8.1	the visible features of an area, including living organisms
large intestine	4.6	an organ, otherwise known as the colon, which is the last part of the digestive system
latitude	8.3	a measurement north or south of the equator
left hemisphere (brain)	9.1, 9.3	the left cerebral hemisphere of the brain
lipid	3.1	a special type of fat
live pin	11.3	the pin of an electrical plug attached to the live wire
long-term memory	9.4	memory stored as meaning that lasts between 30 seconds and a lifetime
lung	7.3	an organ of the body where breathing occurs
lung volume	7.3	the total amount of air that the lungs can hold
magnet	2.2	a material which produces a magnetic field
magnetic field	2.2	a region where an attractive or a repulsive force can be felt due to a magnet or electric current
malnutrition	4.1	a medical condition when a body does not receive a balanced diet
matter	1.1	anything that occupies space
medulla	9.1	the lower part of the brain stem; it controls unconscious actions such as heart rate and relays nerve signals between the brain and spinal cord
memory	9.4	the brain's ability to store, remember and recall information

Word / phrase	Unit	Explanation
metamorphic	8.2, 8.3	a type of rock which has been formed due to great heat or pressure
meteor	3.6	a piece of rock or dust that burns up in the Earth's atmosphere
meteorite	3.6	a natural object from space that survives travelling through the Earth's atmosphere and colliding with its surface
meter	6.2	an instrument used to measure
microbe	10.1	tiny organisms or micro-organisms, generally too small to be seem with the naked eye. They include viruses, bacteria, fungi and protozoa
mid brain	9.1	part of the brain stem that connects the forebrain and brainstem and controls sensory processes
mineral	3.2, 5.4	a natually occuring inorganic material
minerals (in food)	4.1	substances needed in small amounts for the body to remain healthy
mnemonic	4.1, 9.5	a memory aid that is created to help us to remember information
molecule	1.7, 1.8	a group of atoms that are chemically joined - the smallest particle of a compound
nebulae	8.4	huge clouds of dust and gas
neuron	9.1, 9.4, 9.5	also called a nerve cell that is part of the nervous system, these cells process and send electrical information through the brain
neutral pin	11.3	the pin of an electrical plug attached to the neutral wire
neutron	1.5	a subatomic particle in the nucleus with no electric charge
noble gases	1.6	a family of elements in group 8 of the Periodic Table
non-renewable energy	2.2	an energy source which cannot be re-used and hence is running out
nuclear energy	2.3	energy released from the centre of an atom
nuclear fission	2.3	large amount of energy released when a nucleus is split apart
nucleus (pl. nuclei)	1.5	the innermost part of an atom, containing the protons and neutrons
nutrient	4.1	a chemical element or compound needed to maintain an organism
obese	3.1	an accumulation of body fat that may damage health
obesity	4.4	a condition that results from the storage of excess energy from the diet on the body and creates health problems
Ohm's law	6.4	a scientific law describing the relationship between electrical current and voltage
organ	12.1	a group of tissues working together to carry out the same function, e.g. the eye, the heart
osteoporosis	4.4	a disease of bone in which the bone mineral density is lowered
oxide	1.7, 1.8	a chemical compound in which an element is combined with oxygen
oxygen	7.1	a gas that represents 21% of air and is essential for combusion and aerobic respiration
parallel	6.3	two paths which do not cross
particle	1.5	a very small part of a substance
pathogen	10.1	a microbe or other agent that causes disease to its host
period	1.6	the horizontal rows of the Periodic Table
Periodic Table	1.6	a chart of the chemical elements
peristalsis	4.6	the repeated contraction of the smooth muscle of the gut that moves food from mouth to anus
photosynthesis	3.1	the process by which a plant makes its own food
planets	8.4	celestial bodies of a certain size that orbit a star
plasma	7.4	the liquid part of the blood that contains water, dissolved chemicals such as hormones, proteins, food and gases

Word / phrase	Unit	Explanation
platelets	7.4	tiny fragments of cells that are responsible for making blood clot
polymers	1.8, 3.2	large molecules made up from repeating subunits or 'monomers'
pons area	9.1	a bridge-like structure on the brain stem that links different parts of the brain together
population	3.1, 3.4	a group of individuals of the same species that occupy a particular habitat
potential difference	6.2	the correct term for electrical voltage
procedural memory	9.4, 9.5	long-term memory of skills and methods or procedures
proteins	3.1, 4.1	a complex food group made from simpler units of amino acids, these nutrients are necessary for growth and repair
proton	1.5	a subatomic particle in the nucleus with a positive charge
pulse	7.5	a measure of how fast the heart is beating
pus	12.3	a mixture of dead skin cells, white blood cells, and dead or dying bacteria
pyramid of numbers	3.4	the numbers of different organisms in a food chain
reactor	2.3	a device in which nuclear reactions are made to take place to release energy
reagent	4.2	a chemical substance that can be used for testing other substances
rectifier	11.1	a device used to change alternating current into direct current
recycling	3.5	re-using, possibly in a changed form
renewable energy	2.4	an energy source which can be re-used and hence will not run out
resistance	6.1	the opposition to electric current flow
resistor	6.1	an electrical component placed in a circuit to limit the amount of electric current flowing
respiration	4.4, 7.1 7.2, 10.3	a chemical reaction that breaks chemical bonds in glucose to produce energy, carbon dioxide and water and takes place continuously in living cells
right hemisphere (brain)	9.1, 9.3	the right cerebral hemisphere of the brain
risk	4.3	the chance that somebody could be harmed by a specific event
risk assessment	4.3	identifying hazards, evaluating risks and deciding on precautions
root hair cells	3.2	epidermal cells on plant roots
saliva	4.5	an alkaline secretion produced in the mouth that contains amylase enzyme
secretions	4.5	chemical substances that are released from cells
sedimentary	8.2	a type of rock made from sediments, or matter falling to the bottom of a lake or sea
semantic memory	9.4	the memory of meanings, understandings and other learned knowledge
series	6.3	one after the other
short-term memory	9.4	memory that holds only small amounts of information for a short period of up to 30 seconds
silage	3.3	preserved grass for cattle to eat
small intestine	4.6	the part of the gut between the stomach and the colon, where most digestion takes place
starvation	4.1	a condition that results from a lack of food and is a severe form of malnutrition
Stroop effect	9.4	a delay in brain reaction time caused by interference
surface area	3.2	the outside area of a shape or structure
symbol diagram	6.1	a diagram composed of agreed symbols for components rather than actual drawings
thalamus	9.1	part of the brain that relays information to different part of the brain cortex and has a role in regulating sleep

Word / phrase	Unit	Explanation
thermal decomposition	5.2	a chemical reaction in which a chemical substance breaks up into at least two chemical substances when heated
time management	2.6	making the best use of your time by organising it effectively
trachea	7.3	a tube that is surrounded by C-shaped rings of cartilage and carries air from the throat into and away from the lungs
transformer	11.1	a device to increase or decrease electrical voltage
trophic level	3.4	a feeding level in a food chain
turbine	2.2	a device which extracts energy from a moving liquid or gas
variable	8.1	something than can change or be changed in an experiment
variable resistor	6.1	an electrical component whose resistance can be changed
ventricles	7.4	the two chambers present at the base of the heart that pump blood into the two main arteries of the body
virus	10.1	an infectious microbe that is unable to grow or reproduce outside a host cell
Visking tubing	4.5	a special type of semi-permeable membrane with tiny pores that allows only small molecules such as water to pass through by diffusion
vitamin C	9.2	also known as ascorbic acid, this is an essential nutrient that has a role in many reactions in the body; deficiency causes scurvy
vitamins	4.1	nutrients that are needed in small amounts for the body to remain healthy
voltmeter	6.2, 6.4	a device for measuring voltage or potential difference
water (in diet)	4.1	a solvent that is essential for transporting materials in the body and in chemical reactions
watt	11.4	the unit of electrical power, one joule per second
word equation	1.7	a way of representing a chemical reaction
working memory	9.4	short-term memory that is used to store and use information such as for working out a maths problem